Developmental Mathematics:
A Modular Curriculum for North Carolina

GRAPHS AND EQUATIONS OF LINES
DMA 050

ALAN S. TUSSY
CITRUS COLLEGE

R. DAVID GUSTAFSON
ROCK VALLEY COLLEGE

DIANE R. KOENIG
ROCK VALLEY COLLEGE

D1435752

BROOKS/COLE
CENGAGE Learning·

Brazil • Japan • Korea • Mexico • Singapore • Spain • United Kingdom • United States

BROOKS/COLE
CENGAGE Learning

Developmental Mathematics: A Modular Curriculum for North Carolina: Graphs and Equations of Lines
Alan S. Tussy, R. David Gustafson, Diane R. Koenig

Publisher: Charlie Van Wagner

Senior Developmental Editor: Danielle Derbenti

Senior Development Editor for Market Strategies: Rita Lombard

Assistant Editor: Stefanie Beeck

Editorial Assistant: Jennifer Cordoba

Media Editor: Heleny Wong

Marketing Manager: Gordon Lee

Marketing Assistant: Angela Kim

Marketing Communications Manager: Katy Malatesta

Content Project Manager: Jennifer Risden

Creative Director: Rob Hugel

Art Director: Vernon Boes

Print Buyer: Linda Hsu

Rights Acquisitions Account Manager, Text: Mardell Glinksi-Schultz

Rights Acquisitions Account Manager, Image: Don Schlotman

Text Designer: Diane Beasley

Photo Researcher: Bill Smith Group

Illustrators: Lori Heckelman; Graphic World Inc; Integra Software Services

Cover Designers: Ryan and Susan Stranz

Cover Image: Background: © Hemera/Thinkstock. © iStockphoto/Thinkstock.

Compositor: Integra Software Services

For product information and technology assistance, contact us at **Cengage Learning Customer & Sales Support, 1-800-354-9706**

For permission to use material from this text or product, submit all requests online at **www.cengage.com/permissions**

Further permissions questions can be e-mailed to **permissionrequest@cengage.com**

ISBN-13: 978-1-133-87396-9

ISBN-10: 1-133-87396-0

Brooks/Cole
20 Davis Drive
Belmont, CA 94002-3098
USA

Cengage Learning is a leading provider of customized learning solutions with office locations around the globe, including Singapore, the United Kingdom, Australia, Mexico, Brazil, and Japan. Locate your local office at **www.cengage.com/global**

Cengage Learning products are represented in Canada by Nelson Education, Ltd.

To learn more about Brooks/Cole, visit **www.cengage.com/brookscole**

Purchase any of our products at your local college store or at our preferred online store **www.CengageBrain.com**

Printed in the United States of America
1   2   3   4   5   6   7   14   13   12   11   10

To my lovely wife, Liz,
thank you for your insight and encouragement
ALAN S. TUSSY

∎

To my grandchildren:
Daniel, Tyler, Spencer, Skyler, Garrett, and Jake Gustafson
R. DAVID GUSTAFSON

∎

To my husband and my best friend, Brian Koenig
DIANE R. KOENIG

∎

PREFACE

Developmental Mathematics: A Modular Curriculum for North Carolina is a fully integrated learning system that has been aligned to the redesigned curriculum established by the North Carolina Developmental Math Redesign Task Force. With the helpful input from instructors across the state, we have put together a program that presents problems in a meaningful context and explains the "why" behind problem solving in order to promote conceptual and sound mathematical learning. This is one of eight modules for the DMA curriculum, and is supported by a highly customizable online homework system that includes assessment tools, personalized study plans, and algorithmically generated problems to reinforce learning.

One central goal of the North Carolina Redesign Task Force was to create a curriculum with streamlined content in a modular format that could be completed in one academic year. Students can purchase only the modules needed for their developmental math requirements, and can work at a pace that is appropriate for their needs. Instructors can easily use this content with different classroom delivery methods, including self-paced Emporium labs, seated courses, and online or hybrid settings.

Another principle of the new curriculum is to develop students' conceptual understanding of mathematics through the use of contextually based problems. To that end, we have added the following features:

- New **Applied Introductions** have been written to introduce sections that are more applications-driven.
- Within the *Study Sets*, **Applications** problems and examples have been added and written to align with the NCCCS learning outcomes.
- **Concept Extensions** have been written and added to the *Study Sets* to ensure that key concepts meet the NCCCS curriculum.

In addition to new conceptual features that we have written specifically for North Carolina, we have added the following features to help guide students toward mastery of each module:

- **Course Information Sheets** start each module. These offer an explanation of the NCCCS process and ask questions that guide students to the practical knowledge that they will need in order to complete the program.
- **Are You Ready?** quizzes have been added to the beginning of each section to test students on the basic skills they will need in order to be successful with that section.
- **Module Tests**, appearing at the end of each module, have been carefully constructed to include the NCCCS learning outcomes required to pass the mastery test.

All content in these modules is supported by a corresponding prebuilt course in Enhanced WebAssign®, Cengage Learning's powerful online homework solution. Enhanced WebAssign® (EWA) engages students with immediate feedback on algorithmically generated versions of problems for unlimited practice. The *Show My Work* feature allows students to upload a file with the problem worked out, or to use a simple math palette to show their steps–helping you assess whether they understand the steps to solving a problem. The North Carolina EWA course has been prebuilt with a Personalized Study Plan, assignments, homework, and a Pre and Post Test for every module. Instructors can use the prebuilt course as is, or can customize or add material with ease.

A corresponding and fully interactive eBook, the Cengage YouBook, is integrated into the Enhanced WebAssign® course, and offers students convenient access to all module content. This powerful eBook lets you tailor the content to fit your course and provide your students with the ultimate learning experience with note-taking, highlighting, book-marking and search capabilities. Link students to your lecture notes, audio summaries, and engage them through conceptual tutorial videos as well as YouTube clips.

Cengage Learning is committed to providing unparallel service and training for faculty.

- **TeamUP Faculty Programs** help you reach and engage students by offering peer-to-peer consulting on curriculum and assessment, workshops, and professional development conferences.

TeamUP Faculty Program Consultants are a team of educators who understand your challenges whether your classroom is on-ground, online, or both.

Cengage Learning's team of **Faculty Advisors** are full-time educators and expert teachers in a diverse range of subject areas. They are available to share their experience on using Cengage Learning solutions and instructional best practices developed in their own classroom.

Explore all the ways TeamUP Faculty Programs can help you launch a new program or support your continuous improvement efforts. http://www.cengage.com/teamup/programs/ offers service and support from a dedicated team of experts to ensure your success using Enhanced WebAssign, including help with course set up, and more. http://www.cengage.com/coursecare/

TRUSTED FEATURES

- **Study Sets** found in each section offer a multifaceted approach to practicing and reinforcing the concepts taught in each section. They are designed for students to methodically build their knowledge of the section concepts, from basic recall to increasingly complex problem solving, through reading, writing, and thinking mathematically.

  Vocabulary—Each *Study Set* begins with the important *Vocabulary* discussed in that section. The fill-in-the-blank vocabulary problems emphasize the main concepts taught in the chapter and provide the foundation for learning and communicating the language of algebra.

  Concepts—In *Concepts,* students are asked about the specific subskills and procedures necessary to successfully complete the *Guided Practice* and *Try It Yourself* problems that follow.

  Notation—In *Notation,* the students review the new symbols introduced in a section. Often, they are asked to fill in steps of a sample solution. This strengthens their ability to read and write mathematics and prepares them for the *Guided Practice* problems by modeling solution formats.

  Guided Practice—The problems in *Guided Practice* are linked to an associated worked example or objective from that section. This feature promotes student success by referring them to the proper examples if they encounter difficulties solving homework problems.

  Try It Yourself—To promote problem recognition, the *Try It Yourself* problems are thoroughly mixed and are *not* linked to worked examples, giving students an opportunity to practice decision-making and strategy selection as they would when taking a test or quiz.

Applications—The *Applications* provide students the opportunity to apply their newly acquired algebraic skills to relevant and interesting real-life situations.

Writing—The *Writing* problems help students build mathematical communication skills.

Review—The *Review* problems consist of randomly selected problems from previous chapters. These problems are designed to keep students' successfully mastered skills up-to-date before they move on to the next section.

- **Detailed Author Notes** that guide students along in a step-by-step process appear in the solutions to every worked example.

- **Think It Through** features make the connection between mathematics and student life. These relevant topics often require algebra skills from the chapter to be applied to a real-life situation. Topics include tuition costs, student enrollment, job opportunities, credit cards, and many more.

- **Using Your Calculator** is an optional feature that is designed for instructors who wish to use calculators as part of the instruction in this course. This feature introduces keystrokes and shows how scientific and graphing calculators can be used to solve problems. In the *Study Sets,* icons are used to denote problems that may be solved using a calculator.

ACKNOWLEDGMENTS

We want to express our gratitude to all those who helped with this project: Steve Odrich, Mary Lou Wogan, Paul McCombs, Maria H. Andersen, Sheila Pisa, Laurie McManus, Alexander Lee, Ed Kavanaugh, Karl Hunsicker, Cathy Gong, Dave Ryba, Terry Damron, Marion Hammond, Lin Humphrey, Doug Keebaugh, Robin Carter, Tanja Rinkel, Bob Billups, Jeff Cleveland, Jo Morrison, Sheila White, Jim McClain, Paul Swatzel, Matt Stevenson, Carole Carney, Joyce Low, Rob Everest, David Casey, Heddy Paek, Ralph Tippins, Mo Trad, Eagle Zhuang, and the Citrus College library staff (including Barbara Rugeley) for their help with this project. Your encouragement, suggestions, and insight have been invaluable to us.

We would also like to express our thanks to the Cengage Learning editorial, marketing, production, and design staff for helping us craft this new edition: Danielle Derbenti, Michael Stranz, Kim Fry, Heleny Wong, Charlie Van Wagner, Jill Staut, Liz Kendall, Marc Bove, Gordon Lee, Rita Lombard, Angela Hodge, Angela Kim, Maureen Ross, Jennifer Risden, Vernon Boes, Diane Beasley, Carol O'Connell, Graphic World and Integra Software Services.

Additionally, we would like to say that authoring a textbook is a tremendous undertaking. Producing a product of this scale that is customized to match a brand new curriculum would not have been possible without the thoughtful feedback and support from the following colleagues from throughout North Carolina listed below. Their contributions to this edition have shaped the creation of this book in countless ways.

A special acknowledgment is due to Lisa Key Brown, of Central Carolina Community College. Lisa's experience in the Developmental Math classroom, detailed knowledge of the new North Carolina curriculum, and expertise in using Enhanced WebAssign has been invaluable to us as we have prepared this developmental math program.

Alan S. Tussy
R. David Gustafson
Diane R. Koenig

Patricia C. Rome, *Delgado Community College*
Patricia B. Roux, *Delgado Community College*
Rebecca Rozario, *Brookdale Community College*
John Squires, *Cleveland State Community College*
Sharon Testone, *Onondaga Community College*
Bill Thompson, *Red Rocks Community College*
Barbara Tozzi, *Brookdale Community College*
Donna Tupper, *Community College of Baltimore County–Essex*
Andreana Walker, *Calhoun Community College*
Jane Wampler, *Housatonic Community College*
Arminda Wey, *Brookdale Community College*
Mary Lou Wogan, *Klamath Community College*
Valerie Wright, *Central Piedmont Community College*
Kevin Yokoyama, *College of the Redwoods*
Mary Young, *Brookdale Community College*

ABOUT THE AUTHORS

Alan S. Tussy

Alan Tussy teaches all levels of developmental mathematics at Citrus College in Glendora, California. He has written nine math books—a paperback series and a hardcover series. A meticulous, creative, and visionary teacher who maintains a keen focus on his students' greatest challenges, Alan Tussy is an extraordinary author, dedicated to his students' success. Alan received his Bachelor of Science degree in Mathematics from the University of Redlands and his Master of Science degree in Applied Mathematics from California State University, Los Angeles. He has taught up and down the curriculum from Prealgebra to Differential Equations. He is currently focusing on the developmental math courses. Professor Tussy is a member of the American Mathematical Association of Two-Year Colleges.

R. David Gustafson

R. David Gustafson is Professor Emeritus of Mathematics at Rock Valley College in Illinois and coauthor of several best-selling math texts, including Gustafson/Frisk's *Beginning Algebra, Intermediate Algebra, Beginning and Intermediate Algebra: A Combined Approach, College Algebra,* and the Tussy/Gustafson developmental mathematics series. His numerous professional honors include Rock Valley Teacher of the Year and Rockford's Outstanding Educator of the Year. He earned a Master of Arts from Rockford College in Illinois, as well as a Master of Science from Northern Illinois University.

Diane R. Koenig

Diane Koenig received a Bachelor of Science degree in Secondary Math Education from Illinois State University in 1980. She began her career at Rock Valley College in 1981, when she became the Math Supervisor for the newly formed Personalized Learning Center. Earning her Master's Degree in Applied Mathematics from Northern Illinois University, Ms. Koenig in 1984 had the distinction of becoming the first full-time woman mathematics faculty member at Rock Valley College. In addition to being nominated for AMATYC's Excellence in Teaching Award, Diane Koenig was chosen as the Rock Valley College Faculty of the Year by her peers in 2005, and, in 2006, she was awarded the NISOD Teaching Excellence Award as well as the Illinois Mathematics Association of Community Colleges Award for Teaching Excellence. In addition to her teaching, Ms. Koenig has been an active member of the Illinois Mathematics Association of Community Colleges (IMACC). As a member, she has served on the board of directors, on a state-level task force rewriting the course outlines for the developmental mathematics courses, and as the association's newsletter editor.

Module 5: Graphs and Equations of Lines

DMA 050

Kim Steele/Photodisc/Getty Images

from *Campus to Careers*

Postal Service Mail Carrier

Mail carriers follow schedules as they collect and deliver mail to homes and businesses. They must have the ability to quickly and accurately compare similarities and differences among sets of letters, numbers, objects, pictures, and patterns. They also need to have strong problem-solving skills to redirect mislabeled letters and packages. Mail carriers weigh items on postal scales and make calculations with money as they read postage rate tables.

In **Problem 19** of **Study Set 5.1**, you will see how a mail carrier must be able to read a postal rate table and know American units of weight to determine the cost to send a package using priority mail.

JOB TITLE:
Postal Service Mail Carrier

EDUCATION: A high school diploma (or equivalent) and a passing score on a written exam are required.

JOB OUTLOOK: Competition for jobs is high since positions usually come open only upon retirement of current mail carriers.

ANNUAL EARNINGS: Average (mean) salary $51,390

FOR MORE INFORMATION:
http://stats.bls.gov/oes/current/oes435052.htm

Course Information Sheet

Overview

Module 5: Graphs and Equations of Lines is one of the eight modules that make up the North Carolina Community College System Developmental Math Program. This program is for students who want to meet the prerequisites for the math requirements for their two year degree, or for those who are planning to transfer to a college or university. It is designed to allow you to complete the required developmental math courses at a pace that is appropriate to your needs and knowledge.

Placement

The diagnostic test that you took to enter the NCCCS Developmental Math Program has indentified your mathematical strengths and weaknesses. The test results that you received indicate which of the eight modules you are required to complete before you can enroll in more advanced mathematics courses, such as Precalculus and Statistics. It is important to note that any modules you are required to take must be taken in numerical order. For example, if the diagnostic test indicated that you need to take Modules 5 and 6, you must successfully complete Module 5 before you can register for Module 6.

Mastery

A core principle of the NCCCS Developmental Math Program is the concept of mastery of the material. To show mastery, students need to successfully complete all coursework in a module, as well as pass a final assessment exam.

Getting started

Starting a new course can be exciting, but it might also make you a bit nervous. In order to be successful, you need a plan. Here are some suggestions: Make time for the course, know what is expected, build a support system. You can begin to form your personal plan for success by answering questions on the next page.

©iStockphoto/Thinkstock

1. What is your instructor's name? What is his/her phone number and email address?

2. When and where does your class meet?

3. What are the days and times of your instructor's office hours? Where does he/she hold office hours?

4. Does your campus have a math tutoring center? If so, where is it located and what are its hours of operation? Is the tutoring free? Do you need your instructor to sign a form before you begin at the tutoring center?

5. What other ways are there for you to receive additional help with this module?

6. What are the names, phone numbers, and email addresses of three students in your class that you can contact for help if you have missed class, want to form a study group, or have questions regarding a homework assignment?

7. How many hours does your instructor feel you should expect to spend on this course each week?

8. Did you write down your WebAssign user id and password in a safe place where you can find it should you forget?

9. On what day and at what time is the final module assessment exam?

10. What percent correct is needed to pass the final module assessment exam? How many times can the final assessment exam be taken?

Objectives

1 Read tables.

2 Read bar graphs.

3 Read pictographs.

4 Read circle graphs.

5 Read line graphs.

6 Read histograms and frequency polygons.

SECTION **5.1**

Reading Graphs and Tables

ARE YOU READY?

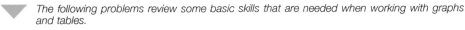

The following problems review some basic skills that are needed when working with graphs and tables.

1. What number is 12% of 80?

2. Evaluate:
$100 - (14 + 25 + 3 + 2 + 8)$

3. How much greater than 32,550 is 50,650?

4. What fraction of the figure is shaded?

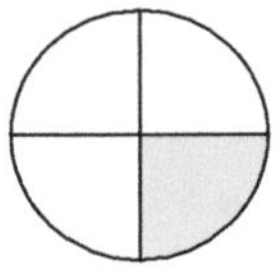

We live in an information age. Never before have so many facts and figures been right at our fingertips. Since information is often presented in the form of tables or graphs, we need to be able to read and make sense of data displayed in that way.

The following **table, bar graph,** and **circle graph** (or **pie chart**) show the results of a shopper survey. A large sample of adults were asked how far in advance they typically shop for a gift. In the bar graph, the length of a bar represents the percent of responses for a given shopping method. In the circle graph, the size of a colored region represents the percent of responses for a given shopping method.

Shopper Survey

How far in advance gift givers typically shop

A Table
Survey responses

Time in advance	Percent
A month or longer	8%
Within a month	12%
Within 3 weeks	12%
Within 2 weeks	23%
Within a week	41%
The same day as giving it	4%

A Bar Graph
Survey responses

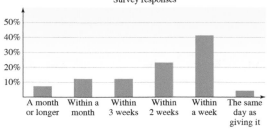

A Circle Graph
Survey responses

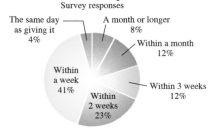

(*Source:* Harris interactive online study via QuickQuery for Gifts.com)

It is often said that a picture is worth a thousand words. That is the case here, where the graphs display the results of the survey more clearly than the table. It's easy to see from the graphs that most people shop within a week of when they need to purchase a gift. It is also apparent that same-day shopping for a gift was the least popular response. That information also appears in the table, but it is just not as obvious.

1   Read tables.

Data are often presented in tables, with information organized in **rows** and **columns.** To read a table, we must find the *intersection* of the row and column that contains the desired information.

EXAMPLE 1   *Postal Rates*   Refer to the table below of priority mail postal rates for letters, large envelopes, and packages. Find the cost of mailing an $8\frac{1}{2}$-pound package by priority mail to postal zone 4.

Postage Rate for Priority Mail 2012

Weight Not Over (pounds)	Local, 1 & 2	Zones 3	4	5	6	7	8
1	$5.20	$5.25	$5.35	$5.50	$5.65	$5.90	$6.30
2	5.30	5.65	6.30	8.05	8.75	9.45	10.40
3	6.05	6.95	8.05	9.70	10.95	11.80	13.85
4	6.85	8.15	9.20	12.85	14.05	15.00	16.70
5	8.10	9.35	10.55	14.55	16.05	17.25	19.25
6	8.95	10.30	11.85	16.20	18.00	19.35	21.75
7	9.50	11.20	12.75	18.05	19.90	21.80	24.45
8	10.20	12.20	14.25	19.60	21.85	24.00	27.40
9	10.85	13.15	**15.45**	21.25	23.80	26.00	30.50
10	11.60	14.15	16.85	23.00	25.70	28.60	33.20
11	12.40	15.10	18.15	24.80	27.60	31.55	36.45
12	13.25	16.20	19.45	26.60	30.00	34.10	39.15

source: usps.com

Strategy   We will read the number at the intersection of the 9th row and the column labeled Zone 4.

WHY   Since $8\frac{1}{2}$ pounds is more than 8 pounds, we cannot use the 8th row. Since $8\frac{1}{2}$ pounds does not exceed 9 pounds, we use the 9th row of the table.

Solution
The number at the intersection of the 9th row (in red) and the column labeled Zone 4 (in blue) is 15.45 (in purple). This means it would cost $15.45 to mail the $8\frac{1}{2}$-pound package by priority mail.

Self Check 1

POSTAL RATES   Refer to the table of priority mail postal rates. Find the cost of mailing a 3.75-pound package by priority mail to postal zone 8.

Now Try   Problem 17

2   Read bar graphs.

Another popular way to display data is to use a **bar graph** with bars drawn vertically or horizontally. The relative heights (or lengths) of the bars make for easy comparisons of values. A horizontal or vertical line used for reference in a bar graph is called an **axis.** The **horizontal axis** and the **vertical axis** of a bar graph serve to frame the graph, and they are scaled in units such as years, dollars, minutes, pounds, and percent.

Self Check 2

SPEED OF ANIMALS Refer to the bar graph of Example 2.
a. What is the maximum speed of a giraffe?
b. How much greater is the maximum speed of a coyote compared to that of a reindeer?
c. Which animals listed in the graph have a maximum speed that is slower than that of a domestic cat?

Now Try **Problem 21**

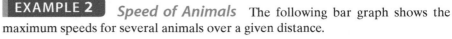

EXAMPLE 2   *Speed of Animals*   The following bar graph shows the maximum speeds for several animals over a given distance.

a. What animal in the graph has the fastest maximum speed?
b. What animal in the graph has the slowest maximum speed?
c. How much greater is the maximum speed of a lion compared to that of a coyote?

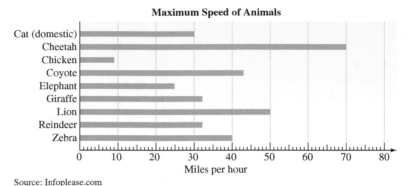

Maximum Speed of Animals

Source: Infoplease.com

Strategy We will locate the name of each desired animal on the vertical axis and move right to the end of its corresponding bar.

WHY Then we can extend downward and read the animal's maximum speed on the horizontal axis scale.

Solution

a. The longest bar in the graph has a length of 70 units and corresponds to a cheetah. Of all the animals listed in the graph, the cheetah has the fastest maximum speed at 70 mph.

b. The shortest bar in the graph has a length of approximately 9 units and corresponds to a chicken. Of all the animals listed in the graph, the chicken has the slowest maximum speed at 9 mph.

c. The length of the bar that represents a lion's maximum speed is 50 units long and the length of the bar that represents a coyote's maximum speed appears to be 43 units long. To find how much greater is the maximum speed of a lion compared to that of a coyote, we subtract

    50 mph – 43 mph = 7 mph   *Subtract the coyote's maximum speed from the lion's maximum speed.*

The maximum speed of a lion is about 7 mph faster than the maximum speed of a coyote.

To compare sets of related data, groups of two (or three) bars can be shown. For **double-bar** or **triple-bar graphs**, a **key** is used to explain the meaning of each type of bar in a group.

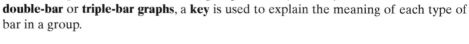

EXAMPLE 3   *The U.S. Economy*   The following bar graph shows the total income generated by three sectors of the U.S. economy in each of three years.

a. What income was generated by retail sales in 2000?
b. Which sector of the economy consistently generated the most income?
c. By what amount did the income from the wholesale sector increase from 1990 to 2007?

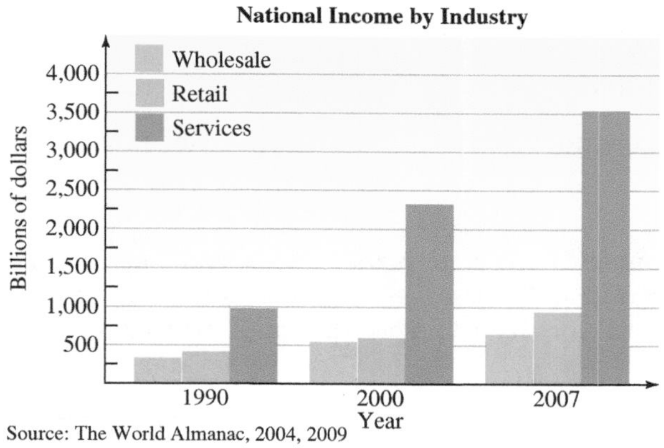

National Income by Industry

Source: The World Almanac, 2004, 2009

THE U.S. ECONOMY Refer to the bar graph of Example 3.

a. What income was generated by retail sales in 1990?

b. What income was generated by the wholesale sector in 2007?

c. In 2000, by what amount did the income from the services sector exceed the income from the retail sector?

Now Try **Problems 25 and 31**

Strategy To answer questions about years, we will locate the correct colored bar and look at the *horizontal axis* of the graph. To answer questions about the income, we will locate the correct colored bar and extend to the left to look at the *vertical axis* of the graph.

WHY The years appear on the horizontal axis. The height of each bar, representing income in billions of dollars, is measured on the scale on the vertical axis.

Solution

a. The second group of bars indicates income in the year 2000. According to the color key, the blue bar of that group shows the retail sales. Since the vertical axis is scaled in units of $250 billion, the height of that bar is approximately 500 plus one-half of 250, or 125. Thus, the height of the blue bar is approximately 500 + 125 = 625, which represents $625 billion in retail sales in 2000.

b. In each group, the green bar is the tallest. That bar, according to the color key, represents the income from the services sector of the economy. Thus, services consistently generated the most income.

c. According to the color key, the orange bar in each group shows income from the wholesale sector. That sector generated about $260 billion of income in 1990 and $700 billion in income in 2007. The amount of increase is the difference of these two quantities.

$700 billion − $260 billion = $440 billion   Subtract the 1990 wholesale income from the 2007 wholesale income.

Wholesale income increased by about $440 billion between 1990 and 2007.

3 Read pictographs.

A **pictograph** is like a bar graph, but the bars are made from pictures or symbols. A **key** tells the meaning (or value) of each symbol.

Pizza Deliveries

The pictograph on the right shows the number of pizzas delivered to the three residence halls on a college campus during final exam week. In the graph, what information does the top row of pizzas give?

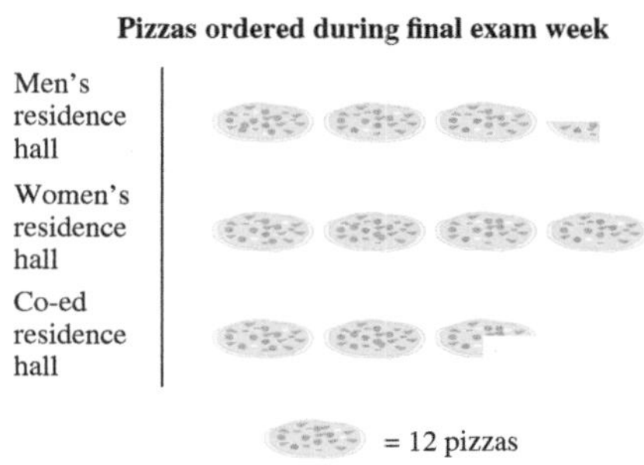

Pizzas ordered during final exam week

= 12 pizzas

PIZZA DELIVERIES In the pictograph of Example 4, what information does the last row of pizzas give?

Now Try **Problems 33 and 35**

Strategy We will count the number of complete pizza symbols that appear in the top row of the graph, and we will estimate what fractional part of a pizza symbol also appears in that row.

WHY The key indicates that each complete pizza symbol represents one dozen (12) pizzas.

Solution

The top row contains 3 complete pizza symbols and what appears to be $\frac{1}{4}$ of another. This means that the men's residence hall ordered $3 \cdot 12$, or 36 pizzas, plus approximately $\frac{1}{4}$ of 12, or about 3 pizzas. This totals 39 pizzas.

> **Caution!** One drawback of a pictograph is that it can be difficult to determine what fractional amount is represented by a portion of a symbol. For example, if the CD shown to the right represents 1,000 units sold, we can only estimate that the partial CD symbol represents about 600 units sold.
>
> $\cdot$ = 1,000 units
>
> $\approx$ 600 units

---

4 Read circle graphs.

In **a circle graph**, regions called **sectors** are used to show what part of the whole each quantity represents.

> **The Language of Mathematics** A *sector* has the shape of a slice of pizza or a slice of pie. Thus, circle graphs are also called **pie charts.**

Self Check 5

GOLD PRODUCTION Refer to the circle graph of Example 5. To the nearest tenth of a million, how many ounces of gold did Russia produce in 2008?

Now Try Problems 37, 41, and 43

EXAMPLE 5   *Gold Production*   The circle graph to the right gives information about world gold production. The entire circle represents the world's total production of 78 million troy ounces in 2008. Use the graph to answer the following questions.

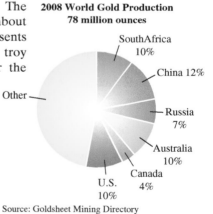

2008 World Gold Production
78 million ounces

Source: Goldsheet Mining Directory

a. What percent of the total was the combined production of the United States and Canada?

b. What percent of the total production came from sources other than those listed?

c. To the nearest tenth of a million, how many ounces of gold did China produce in 2008?

Strategy We will look for the key words in each problem.

WHY Key words tell us what operation (addition, subtraction, multiplication, or division) must be performed to answer each question.

Solution

a. The key word *combined* indicates addition. According to the graph, the United States produced 10% and Canada produced 4% of the total amount of gold in 2008. Together, they produced 10% + 4%, or 14% of the total.

b. The phrase *from sources other than those listed* indicates subtraction. To find the percent of gold produced by countries that are not listed, we add the contributions of all the listed sources and subtract that total from 100%.

$$100\% - (10\% + 12\% + 7\% + 10\% + 4\% + 10\%) = 100\% - 53\% = 47\%$$

Countries that are not listed in the graph produced 47% of the world's total production of gold in 2008.

c. From the graph we see that China produced 12% of the world's gold in 2008. To find the number of ounces produced by China (the amount), we use the method for solving percent problems.

What number	is	12%	of	78?	This is the percent sentence. The units are millions of ounces.
↓	↓	↓	↓	↓	
x	=	12%	·	78	Translate to a percent equation.

Now we perform the multiplication on the right side of the equation.

$x = 0.12 \cdot 78$ Write 12% as a decimal: 12% = 0.12.

$x = 9.36$ Do the multiplication.

Rounded to the nearest tenth of a million, China produced 9.4 million ounces of gold in 2008.

$$
\begin{array}{r}
78 \\
\times\, 0.12 \\
\hline
156 \\
780 \\
\hline
9.36
\end{array}
$$

5 Read line graphs.

Another type of graph, called a **line graph,** is used to show how quantities change with time. From such a graph, we can determine when a quantity is increasing and when it is decreasing.

> **The Language of Mathematics** The symbol ⌇ is often used when graphing to show a break in the scale on an axis. Such a break enables us to omit large portions of empty space on a graph.

EXAMPLE 6   **ATMs** The line graph below shows the number of automated teller machines (ATMs) in the United States for the years 2000 through 2007. Use the graph to answer the following questions.

a. How many ATMs were there in the United States in 2001?

b. Between which two years was there the greatest increase in the number of ATMs?

c. When did the number of ATMs decrease?

d. For which two years was the number of ATMs about the same?

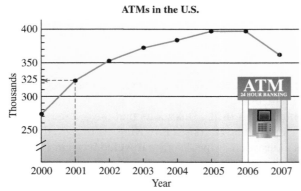

ATMs in the U.S.

Year

Source: The Federal Reserve and *ATM & Debit News*

Self Check 6

ATMS Refer to the line graph of Example 6.

a. Find the increase in the number of ATMs between 2002 and 2003.

b. How many more ATMs were there in the United States in 2007 as compared to 2000?

Now Try Problems 45, 47, and 51

Strategy We will determine whether the graph is rising, falling, or is horizontal.

WHY When the graph rises as we read from left to right, the number of ATMs is increasing. When the graph falls as we read from left to right, the number of ATMs is decreasing. If the graph is horizontal, there is no change in the number of ATMs.

Solution

a. To find the number of ATMs in 2001, we follow the dashed blue line from the label 2001 on the horizontal axis straight up to the line graph. Then we extend directly over to the scale on the vertical axis, where the arrowhead points to approximately 325. Since the vertical scale is in thousands of ATMs, there were about 325,000 ATMs in 2001 in the United States.

b. This line graph is composed of seven line segments that connect pairs of consecutive years. The steepest of those seven segments represents the greatest increase in the number of ATMs. Since that segment is between the 2000 and 2001, the greatest increase in the number of ATMs occurred between 2000 and 2001.

c. The only line segment of the graph that falls as we read from left to right is the segment connecting the data points for the years 2006 and 2007. Thus, the number of ATMs decreased from 2006 to 2007.

d. The data points for the years 2005 and 2006 are both approximately 400,000. Thus, the number of ATMs was about the same for 2005 and 2006.

Two quantities that are changing with time can be compared by drawing both lines on the same graph.

Self Check 7

TRAINS In the graph for Exercise 7, what is train 1 doing at time D?

Now Try **Problems 53, 55, and 59**

EXAMPLE 7   *Trains* The line graph below shows the movements of two trains. The horizontal axis represents time, and the vertical axis represents the distance that the trains have traveled.

a. How are the trains moving at time A?
b. At what time (A, B, C, D, or E) are both trains stopped?
c. At what times have both trains traveled the same distance?

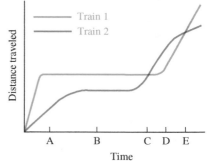

Strategy We will determine whether the graphs are rising or are horizontal. We will also consider the relative positions of the graphs for a given time.

WHY A rising graph indicates the train is moving and a horizontal graph means it is stopped. For any given time, the higher graph indicates that the train it represents has traveled the greater distance.

Solution

The movement of train 1 is represented by the red line, and that of train 2 is represented by the blue line.

a. At time A, the blue line is rising. This shows that the distance traveled by train 2 is increasing. Thus, at time A, train 2 is moving. At time A, the red line is horizontal. This indicates that the distance traveled by train 1 is not changing: At time A, train 1 is stopped.

b. To find the time at which both trains are stopped, we find the time at which both the red and the blue lines are horizontal. At time B, both trains are stopped.

c. At any time, the height of a line gives the distance a train has traveled. Both trains have traveled the same distance whenever the two lines are the same height—that is, at any time when the lines intersect. This occurs at times C and E. ■

6 Read histograms and frequency polygons.

A company that makes vitamins is sponsoring a program on a cable TV channel. The marketing department must choose from three advertisements to show during the program.

1. Children talking about a chewable vitamin that the company makes.

2. A college student talking about an active-life vitamin that the company makes.

3. A grandmother talking about a multivitamin that the company makes.

A survey of the viewing audience records the age of each viewer, counting the number in the 6-to-15-year-old age group, the 16-to-25-year-old age group, and so on. The graph of the data is displayed in a special type of bar graph called a **histogram,** as shown on the right. The vertical axis, labeled **Frequency**, indicates the number of viewers in each age group. For example, the histogram shows that 105 viewers are in the 36-to-45-year-old age group.

A histogram is a bar graph with three important features.

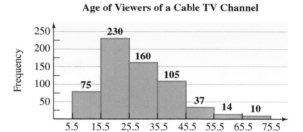

Age of Viewers of a Cable TV Channel

1. The bars of a histogram touch.

2. Data values never fall at the edge of a bar.

3. The widths of each bar are equal and represent a range of values.

The width of each bar of a histogram represents a range of numbers called a **class interval.** The histogram on the right has 7 class intervals, each representing an age span of 10 years. Since most viewers are in the 16-to-25-year-old age group, the marketing department decides to advertise the active-life vitamins in commercials that appeal to young adults.

EXAMPLE 8   *Carry-on Luggage*   An airline weighed the carry-on luggage of 2,260 passengers. The data is displayed in the histogram below.

a. How many passengers carried luggage in the 8-to-11-pound range?

b. How many carried luggage in the 12-to-19-pound range?

Strategy We will examine the scale on the horizontal axis of the histogram and identify the interval that contains the given range of weight for the carry-on luggage.

WHY Then we can read the height of the corresponding bar to answer the question.

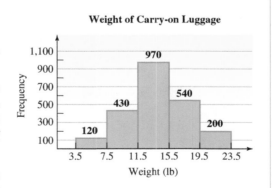

Weight of Carry-on Luggage

Solution

a. The second bar, with edges at 7.5 and 11.5 pounds, corresponds to the 8-to-11-pound range. Use the height of the bar (or the number written there) to determine that 430 passengers carried such luggage.

b. The 12-to-19-pound range is covered by two bars. The total number of passengers with luggage in this range is 970 + 540, or 1,510.

Self Check 8

CARRY-ON LUGGAGE Refer to the histogram of Example 8. How many passengers carried luggage in the 20-to-23-pound range?

Now Try Problem 61

A special line graph, called a **frequency polygon,** can be constructed from the carry-on luggage histogram by joining the center points at the top of each bar. (See the graphs below.) On the horizontal axis, we write the coordinate of the middle value of each bar. After erasing the bars, we get the frequency polygon shown on the right below.

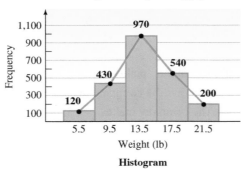

Histogram

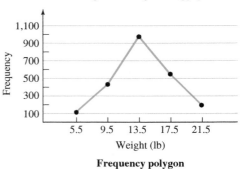

Frequency polygon

ANSWERS TO SELF CHECKS

1. $16.70 **2. a.** 32 mph **b.** 11 mph **c.** a chicken and an elephant **3. a.** about $400 billion **b.** about $700 billion **c.** about $170 billion **4.** 33 pizzas were delivered to the co-ed residence hall. **5.** 5.5 million ounces **6. a.** about 20,000 **b.** about 90,000 **7.** Train 1, which had been stopped, is beginning to move. **8.** 200

SECTION 5.1   STUDY SET

VOCABULARY

For problems 1-6, refer to graphs a through f below. Fill in the blanks with the correct letter.

1. Graph _____ is a bar graph.

2. Graph _____ is a circle graph.

3. Graph _____ is a pictograph.

4. Graph _____ is a line graph.

5. Graph _____ is a histogram.

6. Graph _____ is a frequency polygon.

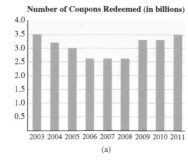

(a)

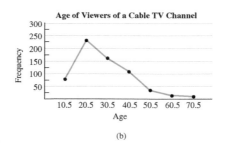

(b)

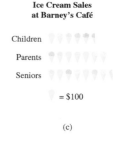

(c)

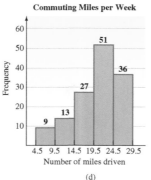

(d)

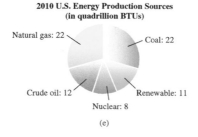

(e)

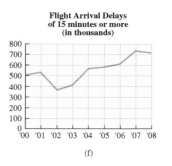

(f)

7. A horizontal or vertical line used for reference in a bar graph is called an _____.

8. In a circle graph, slice-of-pie–shaped figures called _____ are used to show what part of the whole each quantity represents.

CONCEPTS

Fill in the blanks.

9. To read a table, we must find the _____ of the row and column that contains the desired information.

10. The _____ axis and the vertical axis of a bar graph serve to frame the graph, and they are scaled in units such as years, dollars, minutes, pounds, and percent.

11. A pictograph is like a bar graph, but the bars are made from _____ or symbols.

12. Line graphs are often used to show how a quantity changes with _____. On such graphs, we can easily see when a quantity is increasing and when it is _____.

13. A histogram is a bar graph with three important features.

   • The _____ of a histogram touch.
   • Data values never fall at the _____ of a bar.
   • The widths of the bars of a histogram are _____ and represent a range of values.

14. A frequency polygon can be constructed from a histogram by joining the _____ points at the top of each bar.

NOTATION

15. If the symbol 🚌 =1,000 buses, estimate what the symbol 🚌 represents.

16. Fill in the blank: The symbol $\dfrac{}{}$ is used when graphing to show a _____ in the scale on an axis.

GUIDED PRACTICE

Refer to the postal rate table on page 5 to answer the following questions. See Example 1.

17. Find the cost of using priority mail to send a package weighing $7\frac{1}{4}$ pounds to zone 3.

18. Find the cost of sending a package weighing $2\frac{1}{4}$ pounds to zone 5 by priority mail.

19. A woman wants to send a birthday gift and an anniversary gift to her brother, who lives in zone 6, using priority mail. One package weighs 2 pounds 9 ounces, and the other weighs 3 pounds 8 ounces. Suppose you are the woman's mail carrier and she asks you how much money will be saved by sending both gifts as one package instead of two. Make the necessary calculations to answer her question. (Hint: 16 ounces = 1 pound.)

from Campus to Careers
Postal Service Mail Carrier

Kim Steele/Photodisc/Getty Images

20. Juan wants to send a package weighing 6 pounds 1 ounce to a friend living in zone 2. Standard postage would be $3.25. How much could he save by sending the package standard postage instead of priority mail?

Refer to the bar graph below to answer the following questions. See Example 2.

21. List the top three most commonly owned pets in the United States.

22. There are four types of pets that are owned in approximately equal numbers. What are they?

23. Together, are there more pet dogs and cats than pet fish?

24. About many more pet cats are there than pet dogs?

Total Number of Pets Owned in the United States, 2009

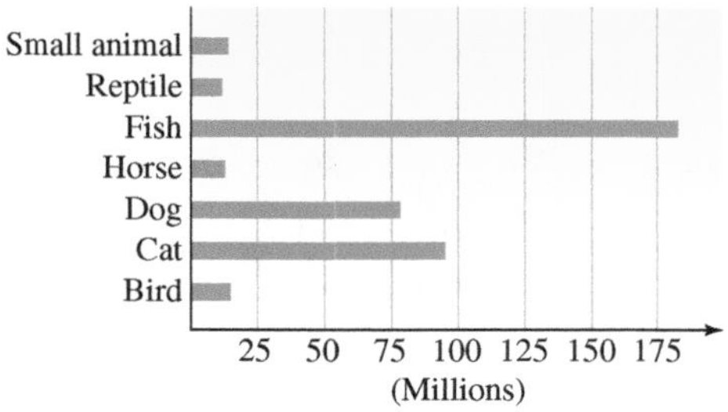

Source: National Pet Owners Survey, AAPA

Refer to the bar graph on the next page to answer the following questions. See Example 3.

25. For the years shown in the graph, has the production of zinc always exceeded the production of lead?

26. Estimate how many times greater the amount of zinc produced in 2000 was compared to the amount of lead produced that year?

27. What is the sum of the amounts of lead produced in 1990, 2000, and 2007?

28. For which metal, lead or zinc, has the production remained about the same over the years?

29. In what years was the amount of zinc produced at least twice that of lead?

30. Estimate the difference in the amount of zinc produced in 2007 and the amount produced in 2000.

31. By how many metric tons did the amount of zinc produced increase between 1990 and 2007?

32. Between which two years did the production of lead decrease?

World Lead and Zinc Production

Source: U.S. Geological Survey

Refer to the pictograph below to answer the following questions. See Example 4.

33. Which group (children, parents, or seniors) spent the most money on ice cream at Barney's Café?

34. How much money did parents spend on ice cream?

35. How much more money did seniors spend than parents?

36. How much more money did seniors spend than children?

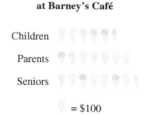

**Ice Cream Sales
at Barney's Café**

Children

Parents

Seniors

= $100

Refer to the circle graph in the next column to answer the following questions. See Example 5.

37. Of the languages in the graph, which is spoken by the greatest number of people?

38. Do more people speak Spanish or French?

39. Together, do more people speak English, French, Spanish, Russian, and German combined than Chinese?

40. Three pairs of languages shown in the graph are spoken by groups of the same size. Which pairs of languages are they?

41. What percent of the world's population speak a language other than the eight shown in the graph?

42. What percent of the world's population speak Russian or English?

43. To the nearest one million, how many people in the world speak Chinese?

44. To the nearest one million, how many people in the world speak Arabic?

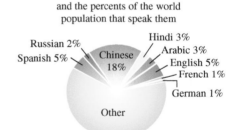

World Languages
and the percents of the world
population that speak them

Russian 2%
Spanish 5%
Chinese 18%
Hindi 3%
Arabic 3%
English 5%
French 1%
German 1%
Other

Estimated world population (2009): 6,771,000,000
Source: *The World Almanac,* 2009

Refer to the line graph on the next page to answer the following questions. See Example 6.

45. How many U.S. ski resorts were in operation in 2004?

46. How many U.S. ski resorts were in operation in 2008?

47. Between which two years was there a decrease in the number of ski resorts in operation? (*Hint:* there is more than one answer.)

48. Between which two years was there an increase in the number of ski resorts in operation? (*Hint:* there is more than one answer.)

49. For which two years were the number of ski resorts in operation the same?

50. Find the difference in the number of ski resorts in operation in 2001 and 2008.

51. Between which two years was there the greatest decrease in the number of ski resorts in operation? What was the decrease?

52. Between which two years was there the greatest increase in the number of ski resorts in operation? What was the increase?

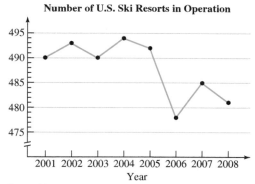

Number of U.S. Ski Resorts in Operation

Source: National Ski Area Assn.

Refer to the line graph below to answer the following questions. See Example 7.

53. Which runner ran faster at the start of the race?

54. At time A, which runner was ahead in the race?

55. At what time during the race were the runners tied for the lead?

56. Which runner stopped to rest first?

57. Which runner dropped his watch and had to go back to get it?

58. At which of these times (A, B, C, D, E) was runner 1 stopped and runner 2 running?

59. Describe what was happening at time E. Who was running? Who was stopped?

60. Which runner won the race?

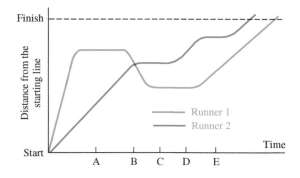

Refer to the histogram and frequency polygon below to answer the following questions. See Example 8.

61. COMMUTING MILES An insurance company collected data on the number of miles its employees drive to and from work. The data are presented in the histogram below.

   a. How many employees have a commute that is in the range of 15 to 19 miles per week?

   b. How many employees commute 14 miles or less per week?

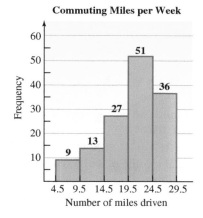

Commuting Miles per Week

62. NIGHT SHIFT STAFFING A hospital administrator surveyed the medical staff to determine the number of room calls during the night. She constructed the frequency polygon below.

   a. On how many nights were there about 30 room calls?

   b. On how many nights were there about 60 room calls?

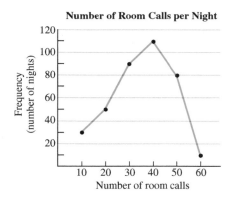

Number of Room Calls per Night

TRY IT YOURSELF

Refer to the 2012 federal income tax table below.

63. FILING A SINGLE RETURN Herb is single and has an adjusted income of $79,250. Compute his federal income tax.

64. FILING A JOINT RETURN Raul and his wife have a combined adjusted income of $57,100. Compute their federal income tax if they file jointly.

65. TAX-SAVING STRATEGY Angelina is single and has an adjusted income of $53,000. If she gets married, she will gain other deductions that will reduce her income by $2,000, and she can file a joint return.

 a. Compute her federal income tax if she remains single.

 b. Compute her federal income tax if she gets married.

 c. How much will she save in federal income tax by getting married?

66. THE MARRIAGE PENALTY A single man with an adjusted income of $80,000 is dating a single woman with an adjusted income of $75,000.

 a. Find the amount of federal income tax each person would pay on their adjusted income.

 b. Add the results from part a.

 c. If they get married and file a joint return, how much federal income tax will they have to pay on their combined adjusted incomes?

 d. Would they have saved on their federal income taxes if they did not get married and paid as two single persons? Find the amount of the "marriage penalty."

Refer to the following bar graph.

67. In which year was the largest percent of flights cancelled? Estimate the percent.

68. In which year was the smallest percent of flights cancelled? Estimate the percent.

69. Did the percent of cancelled flights increase or decrease between 2006 and 2007? By how much?

70. Did the percent of cancelled flights increase or decrease between 2007 and 2008? By how much?

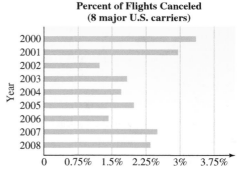

Percent of Flights Canceled
(8 major U.S. carriers)

Source: Bureau of Transportation Statistics

Revised 2012 Tax Rate Schedules

	If TAXABLE INCOME		The TAX is		
		THEN			
	Is Over	But Not Over	This Amount	Plus This %	Of the Amount Over
SCHEDULE X — Single					
	$0	$8,350	$0.00	10%	$0.00
	$8,350	$33,950	$835	15%	$8,350
	$33,950	$82,250	$4,675	25%	$33,950
	$82,250	$171,550	$16,750	28%	$82,250
	$171,550	$372,950	$41,754	33%	$171,550
	$372,950	—	$108,216	35%	$372,950
SCHEDULE Y-1 — Married Filing Jointly or Qualified Widow(er)					
	$0	$16,700	$0.00	10%	$0.00
	$16,700	$67,900	$1,670	15%	$16,700
	$67,900	$137,050	$9,350	25%	$67,900
	$137,050	$208,850	$26,637.50	28%	$137,050
	$208,850	$372,950	$46,741.50	33%	$208,850
	$372,950	—	$100,894.50	35%	$372,950

Refer to the following line graph, which shows the altitude of a small private airplane.

71. How did the plane's altitude change between times B and C?

72. At what time did the pilot first level off the airplane?

73. When did the pilot first begin his descent to land the airplane?

74. How did the plane's altitude change between times D and E?

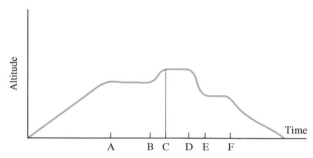

Refer to the following double-bar graph.

75. In which categories of moving violations have violations decreased since last month?

76. Last month, which violation occurred most often?

77. This month, which violation occurred least often?

78. Which violation has shown the greatest decrease in number since last month?

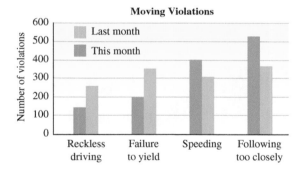

Refer to the following line graph.

79. What were the average weekly earnings in mining for the year 1980?

80. What were the average weekly earnings in construction for the year 1980?

81. Were the average weekly earnings in mining and construction ever the same?

82. What was the difference in a miner's and a construction worker's weekly earnings in 1995?

83. In the period between 2005 and 2010, which occupation's weekly earnings were increasing more rapidly, the miner's or the construction worker's?

84. Did the weekly earnings of a miner or a construction worker ever decrease over a five-year span?

85. In the period from 1980 to 2010, which workers received the greatest increase in weekly earnings?

86. In what five-year span was the miner's increase in weekly earnings the smallest?

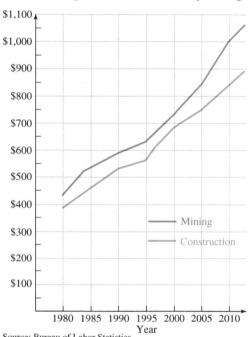

Source: Bureau of Labor Statistics

Refer to the following pictograph.

87. What is the daily parking rate for Midtown New York?

88. What is the daily parking rate for Boston?

89. How much more would it cost to park a car for five days in Boston compared to five days in San Francisco?

90. How much more would it cost to park a car for five days in Midtown New York compared to five days in Boston?

Source: Colliers International

Refer to the following circle graph.

91. What percent of U.S. energy production comes from nuclear energy? Round to the nearest percent.

92. What percent of U.S. energy production comes from natural gas? Round to the nearest percent.

93. What percent of the total energy production comes from renewable and nuclear combined?

94. By what percent does energy produced from coal exceed that produced from crude oil?

2010 U.S. Energy Production Sources
(in quadrillion BTUs)

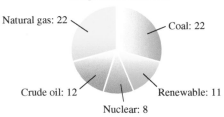

Natural gas: 22   Coal: 22

Crude oil: 12   Renewable: 11

Nuclear: 8

Total production: 75 quadrillion BTUs

Source: Energy Information Administration

95. NUMBER OF U.S. FARMS Use the data in the table below to make a bar graph showing the number of U.S. farms for selected years from 1950 through 2010.

96. SIZE OF U.S. FARMS Use the data in the table below to make a line graph showing the average acreage of U.S. farms for selected years from 1950 through 2010.

Year	Number of U.S. farms (in millions)	Average size of U.S. farms (acres)
1950	5.6	213
1960	4.0	297
1970	2.9	374
1980	2.4	426
1990	2.1	460
2000	2.2	436
2010	2.2	418

Source: U.S. Dept. of Agriculture

97. COUPONS Each coupon value shown in the table below provides savings for shoppers. Make a line graph that relates the original price (in dollars, on the horizontal axis) to the sale price (in dollars, on the vertical axis).

Coupon value: amount saved	Original price of the item
$10	$100, but less than $250
$25	$250, but less than $500
$50	$500 or more

98. DENTISTRY To study the effect of fluoride in preventing tooth decay, researchers counted the number of fillings in the teeth of 28 patients and recorded these results:

3, 7, 11, 21, 16, 22, 18, 8, 12, 3, 7, 2, 8, 19, 12, 19, 12, 10, 13, 10, 14, 15, 14, 14, 9, 10, 12, 13

Tally the results by completing the table. Then make a histogram. The first bar extends from 0.5 to 5.5, the second bar from 5.5 to 10.5, and so on.

Number of fillings	Frequency
1–5	
6–10	
11–15	
16–20	
21–25	

CONCEPT EXTENSIONS

*Refer to the graph below which shows changes in the water level at Blewett Falls Lake, North Carolina, for June 1, 2012. When the lake is full, the water level is 178.1 feet above sea level. Since water level readings were taken every hour, on the hour, the data creates what is known as a **step graph**. The graph looks like a staircase because it only shows the changes in one-hour time intervals, not as a continuous change in the water level.*

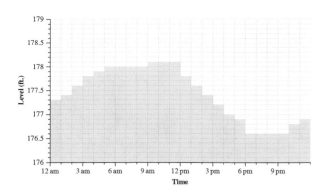

99. What was the water level at 3:00am? What was the water level at 3:00pm?

100. What was the water level when the day began? What was the water level when the day ended?

101. Between 11:00am and noon, by how much did the water level fall?

102. Between 9:00pm and 10:00pm, by how much did the water level rise?

103. What was the highest level the water reached? What was the lowest level the water reached?

104. At what hour was the water level the same as it was at 2:00am?

105. In the evening, when did the greatest hourly decrease in the water level occur? What was the decrease?

106. Between midnight and 11:00am, what was the net increase in the water level?

WRITING

107. What kind of presentation (table, bar graph, line graph, circle graph, pictograph, or histogram) is most appropriate for displaying each type of information? Explain your choices.

- The percent of students at a college, classified by major

- The percent of biology majors at a college each year since 1970

- The number of hours a group of students spent studying for final exams

- The ethnic populations of the ten largest cities

- The average annual salary of corporate executives for ten major industries

108. Explain why a histogram is a special type of bar graph.

SECTION 5.2
Applications Introduction Paired Data

We often deal with **paired data** in our everyday lives. For example, each time you fill up the tank of your car with gasoline, the number of gallons that you pump is paired with the cost that you must pay. Each seven-digit phone number that you call is paired with an area code. For tax purposes, each year that you work is paired with the amount of money that you earn.

One way to present paired data is in a graph. To graph paired data, we begin with two perpendicular lines, called **axes** (pronounced "ak – sez"). The singular form of the word *axes* is **axis**. The **horizontal axis** and the **vertical axis** of a graph each have a quantity associated with them, such as time, weight, or distance. Together, the axes, and the flat **plane** in which they lie create what is called a **coordinate system**.

1. BLOOD TRANSFUSIONS The illustration below is a type of coordinate system. The horizontal axis, labeled "Red cells of donor," displays the possible blood groups, AB, A, B, and O, that a donor might have. The vertical axis, labeled "Serum of recipient," displays the possible blood groups that the transfusion recipient might have. The red boxes show which pairs of blood groups can be mixed without clumping occurring. List the possible pairs of blood types that do not clump when combined. Use the form (donor blood type, recipient blood type) to describe each pair. For example, (A, AB) is one possible pair.

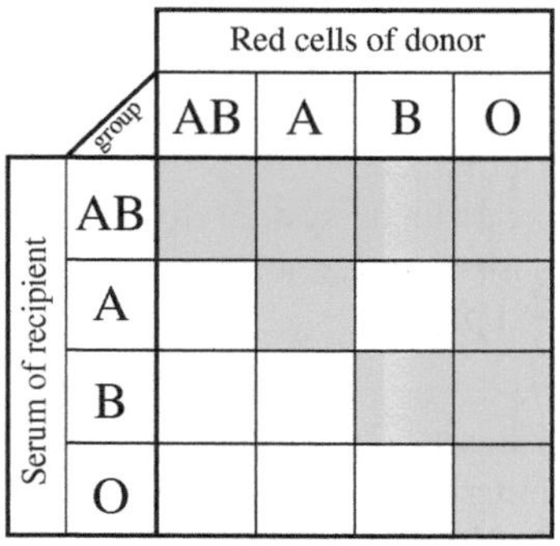

2. **MULTICULTURAL STUDIES** Social scientists use a type of coordinate system shown below to classify cultures. The amount of group/family loyalty in a culture is measured on the horizontal *group* axis. The amount of social mobility is measured on the vertical *social grid* axis. In the diagram, four cultures are classified. In which culture, R, S, T, or U, would you expect that

   a. anyone can grow up to be president, and parents expect their children to get out on their own as soon as possible?
   b. only the upper class attends college, and people must marry within their own social class?

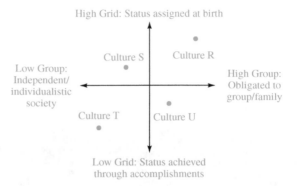

As we saw in problem 1, paired data can be written within parentheses to create what are called **coordinate pairs.** We separate the **first coordinate** and the **second coordinate** of a coordinate pair using a comma. Some other examples of coordinate pairs are: $(3, 8), (-6, 11)$, and $\left(\frac{1}{2}, 7.3\right)$. It is important to note that the order of the coordinates is important. For example, $(3, 8)$ and $(8, 3)$ are different coordinate pairs. For this reason, coordinate pairs are called **ordered pairs**.

3. **ROAD MAPS** Maps have a built-in coordinate system to help locate cities. Use the map below to find the coordinates of these cities in South Carolina: Jonesville, Easley, Hodges, and Union. Express each answer in the form (number, letter).

4. **HURRICANES** A coordinate system that designates the location of places on the surface of Earth uses a series of latitude and longitude lines, as shown in the illustration on the next page.

   a. In 2005, Hurricane Katrina devastated New Orleans. If we list longitude first, what are the coordinates of New Orleans, expressed as an ordered pair?
   b. In August 1992, Hurricane Andrew destroyed Homestead, Florida. Estimate the coordinates of Homestead.
   c. Estimate the coordinates of where Hurricane Andrew hit Louisiana.

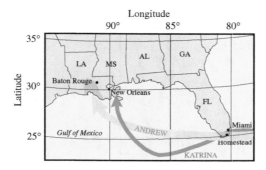

5. THEATER SEATING Your ticket at the theater is for seat B-10. Locate your seat on the diagram.

6. PANTS SALE In the illustration below, an X indicates the sizes of jeans that a store has in stock. List the jeans sizes that are not available as ordered pairs of the form (waist, length).

These pants in your size or they're free. Guaranteed!*

Stonewash jeans, $31.99–$39.99

*Our size guarantee is good only for the following sizes:

Waist	30	31	32	33	34	36	38
Length 30	X	X	X	X	X	X	
32		X	X	X	X	X	X
34			X	X	X	X	X

7. AUTOMATION A robot can be programmed to make welds on a car frame. To do this, an imaginary coordinate system is superimposed on the side of the car. Using the commands Up, Down, Left, and Right, write a set of instructions for the robot arm to move from its beginning position to weld the points A, B, C, and D, in that order.

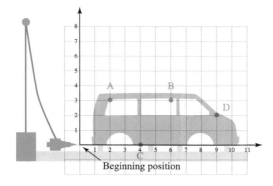

8. THE GLOBE A coordinate system that is used to locate places on the surface of Earth uses a series of curved lines running north and south and east and west, as shown on the next page. List the cities in order, beginning with the one that is farthest east on this map.

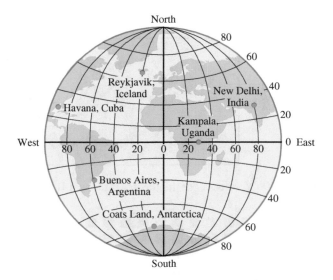

9. DICE The red point in figure (a) represents one of the 36 possible outcomes when two fair dice are rolled a single time. Draw the correct number of dots on the top face of each die in figure (b) to illustrate this outcome.

(a)   (b)

10. PSYCHOLOGY The result of a personal profile test taken by an employee is plotted as an ordered pair on the grid below. The test shows whether the employee is more task oriented or people oriented. From the result, would you expect the employee to *agree* or *disagree* with each of the following statements?

a. Completing a project is almost an obsession with me, and I cannot be content until I am finished.

b. Even if I'm in a hurry while running errands, I will stop to talk with a friend.

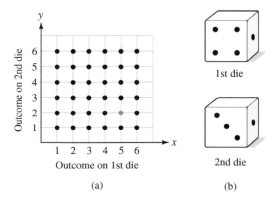

SECTION 5.2

The Rectangular Coordinate System

Objectives

1. Construct a rectangular coordinate system.
2. Plot ordered pairs and determine the coordinates of a point.
3. Graph paired data.
4. Read line graphs.
5. Read step graphs.

ARE YOU READY?

The following problems review some basic skills that are needed when graphing ordered pairs.

1. Graph each number in the set $\left\{\frac{7}{3}, -3, 0, 4, -1.5\right\}$ on a number line.

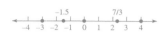

2. a. What number is 8 units to the right of 0 on a number line?

b. What number is 3.5 units to the left of 0 on a number line?

3. List the first four Roman numerals.

4. Write $\frac{9}{2}$ and $-\frac{11}{3}$ in mixed-number form.

It is often said, "A picture is worth a thousand words." In this section, we will show how numerical relationships can be described using mathematical pictures called **graphs.** We will also show how graphs are constructed and how we can obtain information from them.

1 Construct a rectangular coordinate system.

When designing the Gateway Arch in St. Louis, architects created a mathematical model called a **rectangular coordinate graph.** This graph, shown below, is drawn on a grid called a **rectangular coordinate system.** This coordinate system is also called a **Cartesian coordinate system,** after the 17th-century French mathematician René Descartes.

© David R. Frazier Photolibrary Inc./Alamy

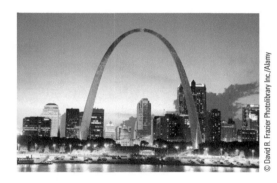

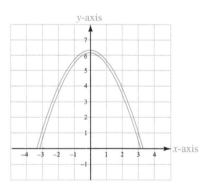

Scale: 1 unit = 100 ft

A rectangular coordinate system is formed by two perpendicular number lines. The horizontal number line is called the ***x*-axis,** and the vertical number line is called the ***y*-axis.** On the x-axis, the positive direction is to the right. On the y-axis, the positive direction is upward. The scale on each axis should fit the data. For example, the axes of the graph of the arch are scaled in units of 100 feet.

> ***Success Tip*** If no scale is indicated on the axes, we assume that the axes are scaled in units of 1.

The point where the axes intersect is called the **origin.** This is the zero point on each axis. The axes form a **coordinate plane,** and they divide it into four regions called **quadrants,** which are numbered counterclockwise using Roman numerals as shown to the right. The axes are not considered to be in any quadrant.

Each point in a coordinate plane can be identified by an **ordered pair** of real numbers x and y written in the form (x, y). The first number, x, in the pair is called the **x-coordinate,** and the second number, y, is called the **y-coordinate.** The numbers in the pair are called the **coordinates** of the point. Some examples of such pairs are $(3, -4)$, $\left(-1, \frac{3}{2}\right)$, and $(0, 2.5)$.

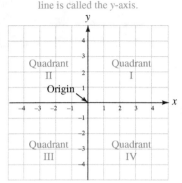

The vertical number line is called the y-axis.

The horizontal number line is called the x-axis.

$$(3, -4)$$
↑ ↑

The x-coordinate is listed first.　The y-coordinate is listed second.

> **Caution!** Do not be confused by this new use of parentheses. The notation $(3, -4)$ represents a point on the coordinate plane, whereas $3(-4)$ indicates multiplication. Also, don't confuse the ordered pair with interval notation.

2 Plot ordered pairs and determine the coordinates of a point.

The process of locating a point in the coordinate plane is called **graphing** or **plotting** the point. In the figure to the right, we use two blue arrows to show how to graph the point with coordinates of $(3, -4)$. Since the x-coordinate, 3, is positive, we start at the origin and move 3 units to the *right* along the x-axis. Since the y-coordinate, -4, is negative, we then move *down* 4 units and draw a dot. The graph of $(3, -4)$ lies in quadrant IV.

Two red arrows are used to show how to plot the point $(-4, 3)$. We start at the origin, move 4 units to the *left* along the x-axis, and then move *up* 3 units and draw a dot. The graph of $(-4, 3)$ lies in quadrant II.

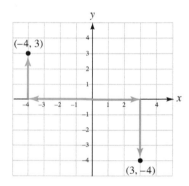

> **The Language of Algebra** Note that the point with coordinates $(3, -4)$ is not the same as the point with coordinates $(-4, 3)$. Since the order of the coordinates of a point is important, we call the pairs **ordered pairs.**

In the figure to the right, we see that the points $(-4, 0)$, $(0, 0)$, and $(2, 0)$ lie on the x-axis. In fact, all points with a y-coordinate of zero will lie on the x-axis. We also see that the points $(0, -3)$, $(0, 0)$, and $(0, 3)$ lie on the y-axis. All points with an x-coordinate of zero lie on the y-axis. We can also see that the coordinates of the origin are $(0, 0)$.

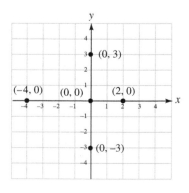

EXAMPLE 1   Plot each point. Then state the quadrant in which it lies or the axis on which it lies.   **a.** $(-2, 3)$ **b.** $\left(-1, -\frac{3}{2}\right)$ **c.** $(0, 2.5)$ **d.** $(4, 2)$

Strategy We will start at the origin and move the corresponding number of units right or left for the *x*-coordinate, then move the corresponding number of units up or down for the *y*-coordinate, to locate the point. Draw a dot at the point.

WHY The coordinates of a point determine its location on the coordinate plane.

Solution

a. Since the *x*-coordinate, -2, is negative, we start at the origin and move 2 units to the *left* along the *x*-axis. Since the *y*-coordinate, 3, is positive, we then move *up* 3 units and draw a dot. The point lies in quadrant II.

b. To plot $\left(-1, -\frac{3}{2}\right)$, we begin at the origin and move 1 unit to the *left* and $\frac{3}{2}$ (or $1\frac{1}{2}$) units *down*. The point lies in quadrant III.

c. To graph $(0, 2.5)$, we begin at the origin and do not move right or left, because the *x*-coordinate is 0. Since the *y*-coordinate is positive, we move 2.5 units *up*. The point lies on the *y*-axis.

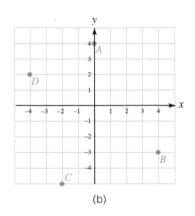

d. To graph $(4, 2)$, we begin at the origin and move 4 units to the *right* and 2 units *up*. The point lies in quadrant I.

Self Check 1

Plot the points:
a. $(2, -2)$ **b.** $(-4, 0)$
c. $\left(1.5, \frac{5}{2}\right)$ **d.** $(0, 5)$

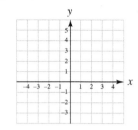

Now Try **Problem 21**

EXAMPLE 2   Find the coordinates of points A, B, C, D, and E plotted in figure (a) below.

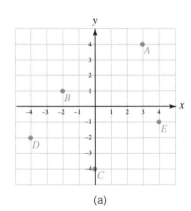

(a)   (b)

Self Check 2

Find the coordinates of each point in figure (b).

Now Try **Problem 25**

Strategy We will start at the origin and count to the right or left on the *x*-axis, and then up or down to reach each point.

WHY The right or left movement gives the *x*-coordinate and the up or down movement gives the *y*-coordinate of the point.

Solution

To find the coordinates of point A, we start at the origin, move 3 units to the right on the *x*-axis, and then 4 units up. The coordinates of point A are $(3, 4)$. The coordinates of the other points are found in the same manner: $B(-2, 1)$, $C(0, -4)$, $D(-4, -2)$, $E(4, -1)$.

3 **Graph paired data.**

Every day, we deal with quantities that are related:

- The time it takes to cook a turkey depends on the weight of the turkey.
- Our weight depends on how much we eat.
- The amount of water in a tub depends on how long the water has been running.

We can use graphs to visualize such relationships. For example, suppose we know the number of gallons of water that are in a tub at several time intervals after the water has been turned on. We can list that information in a table as **paired data.**

The information in the table can be used to construct a graph that shows the relationship between the amount of water in the tub and the time the water has been running. Since the amount of water in the tub depends on the time, we will associate *time* with the *x*-axis and *amount of water* with the *y*-axis.

At various times, the amount of water in the tub was measured and recorded in the table.

Time (min)	Water in tub (gal)	
0	0	→ (0, 0)
1	8	→ (1, 8)
3	24	→ (3, 24)
4	32	→ (4, 32)

x-coordinate   y-coordinate

The data in the table can be expressed as ordered pairs (x, y).

To construct the graph below we plot the four ordered pairs and draw a straight line through the resulting data points. The *y*-axis is scaled in larger units (4 gallons) because the data range from 0 to 32 gallons.

From the graph, we can see that the amount of water in the tub steadily increases as the water is allowed to run. We can also use the graph to make observations about the amount of water in the tub at other times. For example, the dashed line on the graph shows that in 5 minutes, the tub will contain 40 gallons of water.

x	y	(x, y)
0	0	(0, 0)
1	8	(1, 8)
3	24	(3, 24)
4	32	(4, 32)

The data can be listed in a table with headings x, y, and (x, y).

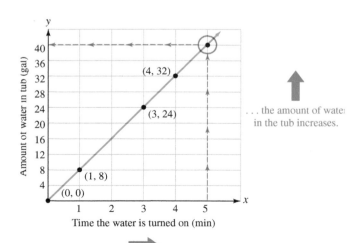

. . . the amount of water in the tub increases.

As the time increases . . .

4 Read line graphs.

Since graphs are a popular way to present information, the ability to read and interpret them is very important.

EXAMPLE 3   *TV Shows*   The graph shows the number of people in an audience before, during, and after the taping of a television show. On the *x*-axis, zero represents the time when taping began. Use the graph to answer the following questions and complete the table.

a. How many people were in the audience when taping began?

b. What was the size of the audience 10 minutes before taping began?

c. At what times were there exactly 100 people in the audience?

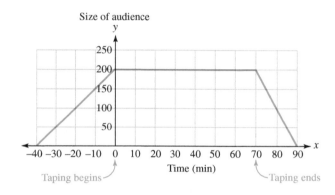

Size of audience

Time (min)

Taping begins

Taping ends

Self Check 3

Use the graph to answer the following questions.
a. At what times were there exactly 50 people in the audience?
b. What was the size of the audience that watched the taping?
c. How long did it take for the audience to leave the studio after the taping ended?

***Now Try* Problems 33 and 34**

Strategy We will use an ordered pair of the form (*time, size of audience*) to describe each situation mentioned in parts a, b, and c.

WHY The coordinates of specific points on the graph can be used to answer each of these questions.

Solution

a. The time when taping began is represented by 0 on the *x*-axis. The point on the graph directly above 0 is (0, 200). The *y*-coordinate indicates that 200 people were in the audience when the taping began. We enter this result in the table at the right.

Time (min)	Size of audience
x	*y*
0	200
−10	150
−20	100
80	100

b. Ten minutes before taping began is represented by −10 on the *x*-axis. The point on the graph directly above −10 is (−10, 150). The *y*-coordinate indicates that 150 people were in the audience 10 minutes before the taping began. We enter this result in the table.

c. We can draw a horizontal line passing through 100 on the *y*-axis. Since this line intersects the graph twice, at (−20, 100) and at (80, 100), there are two times when 100 people were in the audience. The *x*-coordinates of the points tell us those times: 20 minutes before taping began and 80 minutes after. Enter these results in the table.

5 Read step graphs.

The graph below shows the cost of renting a trailer for different periods of time. For example, the cost of renting the trailer for 4 days is $60, which is the y-coordinate of the point (4, 60). The cost of renting the trailer for a period lasting over 4 and up to 5 days jumps to $70. Since the jumps in cost form steps in the graph, we call this graph a **step graph.**

Self Check 4

Use the information in the figure of Example 4 to answer the following:
a. Find the cost of renting the trailer for 1 day.
b. Find the cost of renting the trailer for $4\frac{1}{2}$ days.
c. How long can you rent the trailer if you have $40?

Now Try **Problems 37 and 38**

EXAMPLE 4   Use the information in the figure to answer the following questions. Write the results in a table.

a. Find the cost of renting the trailer for 2 days.
b. Find the cost of renting the trailer for $5\frac{1}{2}$ days.
c. How long can you rent the trailer if you have $50?

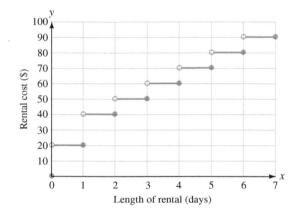

Strategy We will use an ordered pair of the form (*days, rental cost*) to describe each situation mentioned in parts a, b, and c.

WHY The coordinates of specific points on the graph can be used to answer each of these questions.

Solution

a. The solid dot at the end of each step indicates the rental cost for 1, 2, 3, 4, 5, 6, or 7 days. Each open circle indicates that that point is not on the graph. We locate 2 days on the x-axis and move up to locate the point on the graph directly above the 2. Since the point has coordinates (2, 40), a 2-day rental would cost $40. We enter this result in the table below.

b. We locate $5\frac{1}{2}$ days on the x-axis and move straight up to locate the point with coordinates $\left(5\frac{1}{2}, 80\right)$, which indicates that a $5\frac{1}{2}$-day rental would cost $80. We then enter this result in the table.

c. We draw a horizontal line through the point labeled 50 on the y-axis. Since this line intersects one step in the graph, we can look down to the x-axis to find the x-values that correspond to a y-value of 50. From the graph, we see that the trailer can be rented for more than 2 and up to 3 days for $50. The point has coordinates (3, 50). Enter the results in the table.

Length of rental (days) x	Cost (dollars) y
2	40
$5\frac{1}{2}$	80
3	50

ANSWERS TO SELF CHECKS

1.

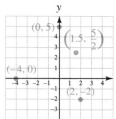

2. $A(0, 4)$, $B(4, -3)$, $C(-2, -5)$, $D(-4, 2)$
3. a. 30 min before and 85 min after taping began
b. 200   **c.** 20 min   **4. a.** $20   **b.** $70   **c.** 2 days

SECTION **5.2**   STUDY SET

VOCABULARY

Fill in the blanks.

1. The point with coordinates $(4, 2)$ can be graphed on a _____ coordinate system.

2. On the rectangular coordinate system, the horizontal number line is called the _____ and the vertical number line is called the _____.

3. On the rectangular coordinate system, the point $(0, 0)$ where the axes cross is called the _____.

4. On the rectangular coordinate system, the axes form the _____ plane.

5. The x- and y-axes divide the coordinate plane into four regions called _____.

6. The pair of numbers $(-1, -5)$ is called an _____ pair.

7. In the ordered pair $\left(-\frac{3}{2}, -5\right)$, $-\frac{3}{2}$ is called the _____ and -5 is called the _____.

8. The process of locating the position of a point on a coordinate plane is called _____ the point.

CONCEPTS

Fill in the blanks.

9. To plot the point with coordinates $(-5, 4.5)$, we start at the _____ and move 5 units to the _____ and then move 4.5 units _____.

10. To plot the point with coordinates $\left(6, -\frac{3}{2}\right)$, we start at the _____ and move 6 units to the _____ and then move $\frac{3}{2}$ units _____.

11. Do $(3, 2)$ and $(2, 3)$ represent the same point?

12. In the ordered pair $(4, 5)$, is the number 4 associated with the horizontal or the vertical axis?

13. In which quadrant do points with a negative x-coordinate and a positive y-coordinate lie?

14. In which quadrant do points with a positive x-coordinate and a negative y-coordinate lie?

15. In the following illustration, fill in the missing coordinate of each highlighted point on the graph of the circle.

a. $\left(4, \quad\right)$
b. $\left(3, \quad\right)$
c. $\left(5, \quad\right)$
d. $\left(-3, \quad\right)$
e. $\left(-5, \quad\right)$
f. $\left(0, \quad\right)$

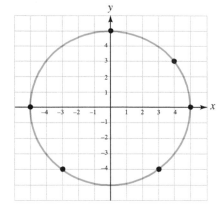

16. In the following illustration, fill in the missing coordinate of each point on the graph of the line.

a. $\left(-4, \quad\right)$
b. $\left(\quad, 0\right)$
c. $\left(\quad, 2\right)$
d. $\left(\quad, -1\right)$
e. $\left(\quad, 1\right)$

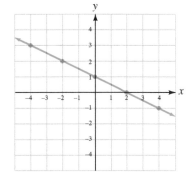

NOTATION

17. Explain the difference between $(3, 5)$, $3(5)$, and $5(3 + 5)$.

18. In the table, which column contains values associated with the vertical axis of a graph?

x	y
2	0
5	-2
-1	$-\frac{1}{2}$

19. Do these ordered pairs name the same point?

$$\left(2.5, -\frac{7}{2}\right), \left(2\frac{1}{2}, -3.5\right), \left(2.5, -3\frac{1}{2}\right)$$

20. Do these ordered pairs name the same point?

$$(-1.25, 4), \left(-1\frac{1}{4}, 4.0\right), \left(-\frac{5}{4}, 4\right)$$

GUIDED PRACTICE

Plot each point on the grid provided. **See Example 1.**

21. $(-3, 4)$
$(4, 3.5)$
$\left(-2, -\frac{5}{2}\right)$

22. $(0, -4)$
$\left(\frac{3}{2}, 0\right)$
$(3, -4)$

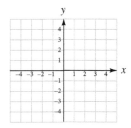

23. $(4, 4)$
$(0.5, -3)$
$(-4, -4)$

24. $(0, 0)$
$(0, 3)$
$(-2, 0)$
$(0, -1)$

Refer to the illustration and determine the coordinates of each point. **See Example 2.**

25. A
26. B
27. C
28. D
29. E
30. F
31. G
32. H

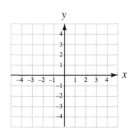

The graph in the illustration gives the heart rate of a woman before, during, and after an aerobic workout. Use the graph to answer problems 33 and 34. **See Example 3.**

33. a. What information does the point $(-10, 60)$ give us?

b. After beginning her workout, how long did it take the woman to reach her training-zone heart rate?

c. What was the woman's heart rate half an hour after beginning the workout?

d. For how long did the woman work out at her training zone?

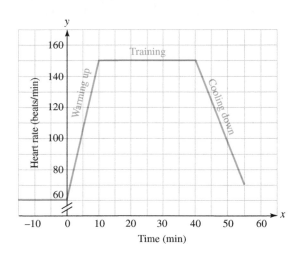

34. a. At what time was her heart rate 100 beats per minute?

b. How long was her cool-down period?

c. What was the difference in the woman's heart rate before the workout and after the cool-down period?

d. What was her approximate heart rate 8 minutes after beginning?

Use the graph to answer each question. **See Example 3.**

35. AIRPLANES The graph on the next page shows the altitudes of a plane at certain times.

a. Where is the plane when $t = 0$?

b. What is the plane doing as t increases from 1 to 2?

c. For how long does the airplane travel at an altitude of 5,000 feet?

d. How much of a descent does the plane begin to make 4 hours after take-off?

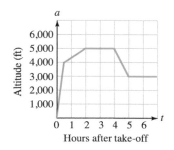

36. SUBMARINES The graph in the following illustration shows the depths of a submarine at certain times.

a. Where is the sub 2 hours after launch?

b. What is the sub doing as increases from 2 to 3?

c. For how long does the sub travel at a depth of 1,000 feet?

d. How large an ascent does the sub begin to make 6 hours after launch?

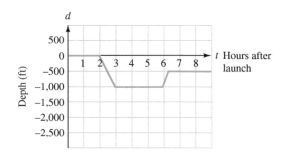

The graph in the illustration below gives the charges for renting a video for certain lengths of time. **See Example 4.**

37. a. Find the charge for a 1-day rental.

b. Find the charge for a 2-day rental.

c. What is the charge if a tape is kept for 5 days?

d. What is the charge if a tape is kept for a week?

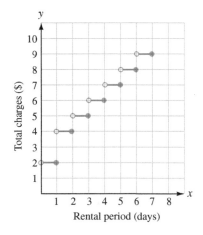

38. TAXIS The following graph gives the fares charged for rides up to 1 mile in length by a taxicab company.

a. What is the fare for a $\frac{1}{2}$-mile ride?

b. Is the fare the same for each $\frac{1}{8}$ mile traveled?

c. What is a fare for a $\frac{7}{10}$-mile long ride?

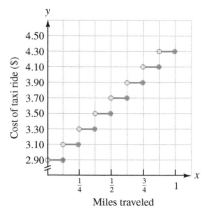

The symbol ⧸ indicates a break in the labeling of the vertical axis. The break enables us to omit a large portion of the grid that would not be used.

CONCEPT EXTENSIONS

39. CAMPUS PARKING Match each daily parking description below with the graph below that best illustrates it. The parking lot holds 500 cars.

a. On Mondays, the parking lot is full by noon. It's impossible to find a parking space until late in the afternoon.

b. On Tuesdays, the lot never gets more than half-full.

c. On Wednesdays, the lot fills up quickly. It empties out around lunchtime but then it fills up fast when the evening classes begin.

d. On Thursdays, it is easy to park in the lot until the evening classes begin. Then it is almost impossible to find a parking space.

e. On Fridays, it is very difficult to find a parking space, unless you arrive early. However, the lot clears out by noon.

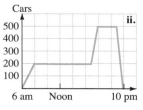

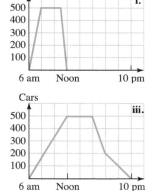

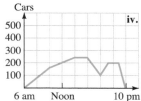

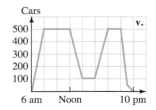

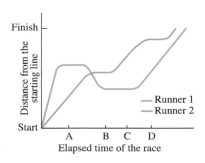

40. Match each description with the graph below that best illustrates it.

  a. You make popcorn in a microwave. The number of pops per second depends on the time since you started the microwave.

  b. You jump off a diving board. Your position in relation to the surface of the water depends on the time since you jumped.

  c. You mow your lawn when it reaches a certain height. The height of the grass depends on the time since you last mowed it.

  d. You pour water into a glass filled with ice. The temperature of the water depends on the time since you poured it.

  e. You run out of gas on a highway and coast to a stop. Your car's speed depends on the time since you ran out of gas.

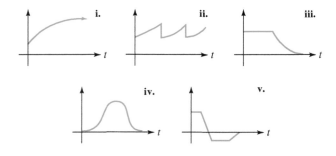

41. LONG-DISTANCE RUNNING Refer to the graph in the next column that describes a two-person race.

  a. Which runner ran faster at the start of the race?

  b. Which runner stopped to rest first?

  c. Which runner dropped his watch and had to go back and get it?

  d. At which of these elapsed times (A, B, C, D) was runner 1 stopped and runner 2 running?

  e. Describe what was happening at time D.

  f. Which runner won the race?

42. ROAST TURKEY Guidelines that appear on the label of a frozen turkey are listed in the table. Draw a step graph that illustrates these instructions.

Size	Time thawing in refrigerator
10 lb to just under 18 lb	3 days
18 lb to just under 22 lb	4 days
22 lb to just under 24 lb	5 days
24 lb to just under 30 lb	6 days

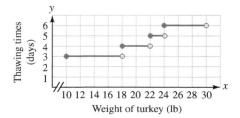

43. EARTHQUAKES The following graph shows the area damaged by an earthquake.

  a. Find the coordinates of the *epicenter* (the source of the quake).

  b. Was damage done at the point $(4, 5)$?

  c. Was damage done at the point $(-1, -4)$?

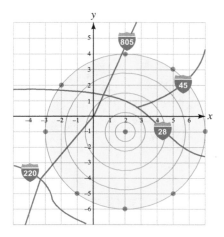

44. GEOGRAPHY The illustration on the next page shows a cross-sectional profile of the Sierra Nevada mountain range.

   a. Estimate the coordinates of blue oak, sagebrush scrub, and tundra using an ordered pair of the form (distance, elevation).

   b. The *tree line* is the highest elevation at which trees grow. Estimate the tree line for this mountain range.

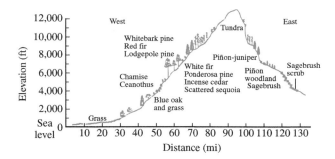

45. BRIDGE CONSTRUCTION Find the coordinates of each rivet, weld, and anchor.

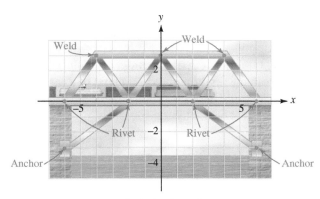

Scale: 1 unit = 8 ft

46. GOLF A golfer is videotaped and then has her swing displayed on a computer monitor so that it can be analyzed. Give the coordinates of the points that are highlighted in red.

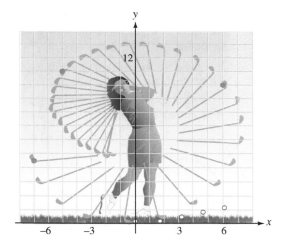

47. GAMES In the game Battleship, the player uses coordinates to drop depth charges from a battleship to hit a hidden submarine. What coordinates should be used to make three hits on the exposed submarine shown? Express each answer in the form (letter, number).

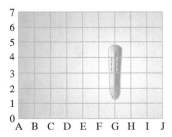

48. MAPS Use coordinates of the form (number, letter) to locate each position on the following map: Rockford, Forreston, Harvard, and the intersection of state Highway 251 and U.S. Highway 30.

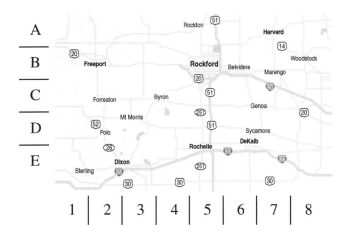

49. WATER PRESSURE The graph shows how the path of a stream of water changes when the hose is held at two different angles.

   a. At which angle does the stream of water shoot up higher? How much higher?

   b. At which angle does the stream of water shoot out farther? How much farther?

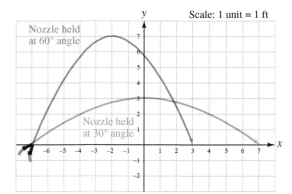

50. MEDICINE Scoliosis is a lateral curvature of the spine that can be detected when a grid is superimposed over an X-ray. In the illustration, find the coordinates of the center points of the indicated vertebrae. Note that T3 means the third thoracic vertebra, L4 means the fourth lumbar vertebra, and so on.

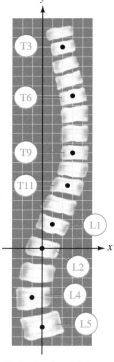

Scale: 1 unit = 0.5 in.

51. DENTISTRY Dentists describe teeth as being located in one of four quadrants as shown below:

   a. How many teeth are located in the upper left quadrant?

   b. Why would the upper left quadrant appear on the right in the illustration?

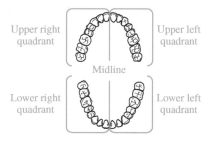

52. GAS MILEAGE The following table gives the number of miles (*y*) that a truck can be driven on *x* gallons of gasoline. Plot the ordered pairs and draw a line connecting the points.

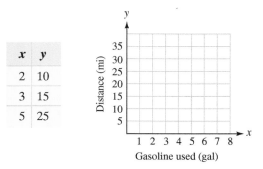

x	y
2	10
3	15
5	25

   a. Estimate how far the truck can go on 7 gallons of gasoline.

   b. How many gallons of gas are needed to travel a distance of 20 miles?

   c. How far can the truck go on 6.5 gallons of gasoline?

53. VALUE OF A CAR The following table shows the value *y* (in thousands of dollars) of a car that is *x* years old. Plot the ordered pairs and draw a line connecting the points.

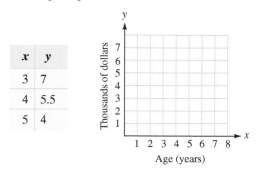

x	y
3	7
4	5.5
5	4

   a. What does the point (3, 7) on the graph tell you?

   b. Estimate the value of the car when it is 7 years old.

   c. After how many years will the car be worth $2,500?

54. BOATING The table below shows the cost to rent a sailboat for a given number of hours. Plot the data in the table as ordered pairs. Then draw a line through the points.

a. How much will it cost to rent the boat for 3 hours?

b. For how long can the boat be rented for $60?

Rental time (hr)	Cost ($)
2	20
4	30
6	40

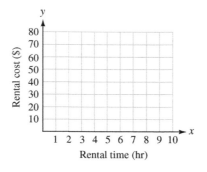

55. AREA Three vertices (corners) of a rectangle are $(2, 1)$, $(6, 1)$, and $(6, 4)$. Find the coordinates of the fourth vertex. Then find the area of the rectangle.

56. AREA Three vertices (corners) of a right triangle are $(-1, -7)$, $(-5, -7)$, and $(-5, -2)$. Find the area of the triangle.

57. LANDMARKS A scale model of the block letter H in the Hollywood sign can be drawn by plotting the following points and connecting them: $(0, 0)$, $(13, 0)$, $(13, 16)$, $(26, 16)$, $(26, 0)$, $(39, 0)$, $(39, 45)$, $(26, 45)$, $(26, 29)$, $(13, 29)$, $(13, 45)$, and $(0, 45)$. The scale is 1 unit on the graph is equal to 1 foot on the actual sign. If a gallon of paint covers 350 square feet, how many gallons are needed to paint the front side of the letter H? Round to the nearest gallon.

58. AIRPLANES Engineers use a coordinate system with 3 axes, as shown on the right. Any point on the airplane can be described by an *ordered triple* of the form (x, y, z). The coordinates of three points on the plane are $(0, 181, 56)$, $(-46, 48, 19)$, and $(84, 94, 24)$. Which highlighted part of the plane corresponds with which ordered triple?

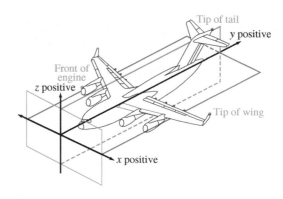

WRITING

59. Explain why the point $(-3, 3)$ is not the same as the point $(3, -3)$.

60. Explain what is meant when we say that the rectangular coordinate graph of the St. Louis Gateway Arch is made up of *infinitely many* points.

61. Explain how to plot the point $(-2, 5)$.

62. Explain why the coordinates of the origin are $(0, 0)$.

63. Use the Internet to perform a search of the name René Descartes. After reading about him, explain how a fly on his bedroom ceiling provided the inspiration for the concept of a rectangular coordinate system.

64. Explain this diagram.

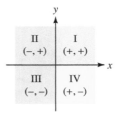

SECTION 5.3

Applications Introduction North Carolina Median Household Income

In 1990, the **median household income*** in North Carolina was $26,329. That means in 1990, one-half of the households had an income less than $26,329 and one-half had an income greater than $26,329. The following tables give the median household income in North Carolina for the years 1990 through 2010.

Year	1990	1991	1992	1993	1994	1995	1996	1997	1998	1999
x-value	0	1	2	3	4	5	6	7	8	9
Income	26,329	26,853	27,771	28,820	30,114	31,979	35,601	35,840	35,838	37,254

Year	2000	2001	2002	2003	2004	2005	2006	2007	2008	2009	2010
x-value	10	11	12	13	14	15	16	17	18	19	20
Income	38,317	38,162	36,515	37,279	40,238	42,056	42,625	44,670	46,549	43,674	43,326

(Source: NCCCS Developmental Math Module DMA 050 Beta version, U.S. Census Bureau,)

1. Examine the data in the first table. Describe any trends for the median household income from 1990 through 1999.

2. Examine the data in the second table. Describe any trends for the median household income from 2000 through 2010.

3. For what years did the median household income stay approximately the same?

4. For what years did the median household income decrease when compared to the previous year?

* *Median household income* includes the income of the householder and all other individuals 15 years old and over in the household, whether they are related to the householder or not.

5. Now graph the data from the two tables on the previous page on the grid below. The years are listed on horizontal axis and the median annual income is listed on the vertical axis. On the horizontal axis, we can simplify the scaling by letting 0 represent 1990, 1 represent 1991, 2 represent 1992, and so on.

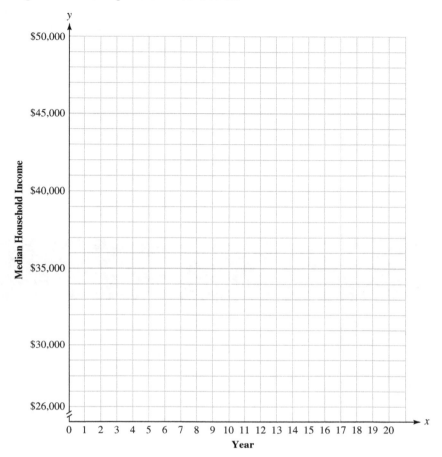

6. Examine the graph above. Describe any trends for the median household income from 1990 through 2010. From the graph, can you make a prediction about what will happen to median household income in the future?

7. We call the graph you constructed in problem 5 a **scatter diagram**. It is often useful to represent the data in a scatter diagram with a straight line called a **line of best fit**. A line of best fit (also called a **trend line**) is a straight line that best represents the data on a scatter diagram. This line may pass through some of the points, none of the points, or all of the points of the graph. Use a ruler or straight-edge to draw a line of best fit on your graph by drawing a straight line that leaves an equal number of points on either side of the line. Note that answers may vary.

Objectives

1. Determine whether an ordered pair is a solution of an equation.
2. Complete ordered-pair solutions of equations.
3. Construct a table of solutions.
4. Graph equations by plotting points.
5. Graph equations that use different variables.

SECTION 5.3

Graphing Equations in Two Variables

ARE YOU READY?

The following problems review some basic skills that are needed when graphing equations in two variables.

1. How many variables does the equation $y = 6x - 5$ contain?

2. Is the following equation true or false?
$$2(3) - 4(-1) = -2$$

3. Evaluate $-6x - 8$ for $x = -3$

4. Evaluate $x^2 + 3$ for $x = 2$

5. Evaluate $|x - 1|$ for $x = -1$.

6. Evaluate x^3 for $x = 2$.

In this section, we will discuss equations that contain two variables. These equations are often used to describe relationships between two quantities. To see a mathematical picture of these relationships, we will construct graphs of their equations.

1 Determine whether an ordered pair is a solution of an equation.

We have previously solved **equations in one variable.** For example, $x - 4 = 3$ is an equation in x. If we add 4 to both sides, we see that $x = 7$ is the solution. To check this, we replace x with 7 and note that the result is a true statement: $3 = 3$.

In this chapter, we extend our equation-solving skills to find solutions of **equations in two variables.** To begin, let's consider $y = x - 1$, an equation in x and y.

A solution of $y = x - 1$ is a pair of values, one for x and one for y, that make the equation true. For example, suppose x is 5 and y is 4. Then we have:

$y = x - 1$ This is the original equation.

 $4 \overset{?}{=} 5 - 1$ Substitute 5 for x and 4 for y.

$4 = 4$ True

Since $4 = 4$ is a true statement, the ordered pair $(5, 4)$ is a solution, and we say that $(5, 4)$ **satisfies** the equation. In general, a *solution of an equation in two variables* is an ordered pair of numbers that makes the equation a true statement.

EXAMPLE 1 Is the ordered pair $(-1, -3)$ a solution of $y = x - 1$?

Strategy We will substitute -1 for x and -3 for y and see whether the resulting equation is true.

WHY An ordered pair is a *solution* of $y = x - 1$ if replacing the variables with the values of the ordered pair results in a true statement.

Solution

$y = x - 1$ This is the original equation.

$-3 \overset{?}{=} -1 - 1$ Substitute -1 for x and -3 for y.

$-3 = -2$ Perform the subtraction: $-1 - 1 = -2$. False

Since $-3 = -2$ is a false statement, $(-1, -3)$ is not a solution of $y = x - 1$. ∎

Self Check 1

Is $(9, 8)$ a solution of
$y = x - 1$?

Now Try Problem 17

EXAMPLE 2 Is the ordered pair $(-6, 36)$ a solution of $y = x^2$?

Strategy We will substitute -6 for x and 36 for y and see whether the resulting equation is true.

WHY An ordered pair is a *solution* of $y = x^2$ if replacing the variables with the values of the ordered pair results in a true statement.

Solution

We substitute -6 for x and 36 for y and see whether the resulting equation is a true statement.

$y = x^2$ This is the original equation.

$36 \overset{?}{=} (-6)^2$ Substitute -6 for x and 36 for y.

$36 = 36$ Find the power: $(-6)^2 = 36$. True

Since the equation $36 = 36$ is true, $(-6, 36)$ is a solution of $y = x^2$. ∎

Self Check 2

Is $(-2, 5)$ a solution of $y = x^2$?

Now Try Problem 19

> **Language of Algebra** Equations in two variables often involve the variables x and y. However, other letters can be used. For example, $a - 3b = 6$ and $n = 2m + 1$ are equations in two variables.

2 Complete ordered-pair solutions of equations.

If only one of the values of an ordered-pair solution is known, we can substitute it into the equation to determine the other value.

EXAMPLE 3 Complete the solution $(-4, \ \ )$ of the equation $y = -x + 2$.

Strategy We will substitute the known x-coordinate of the solution into the given equation.

WHY We can use the resulting equation in one variable to find the unknown y-coordinate of the solution.

Solution

In the ordered pair $(-4, \ \ )$, the x-value is -4; the y-value is not known. To find y, we substitute -4 for x in the equation and evaluate the right side.

$y = -x + 2$ This is the original equation.

$y = -(-4) + 2$ Substitute -4 for x.

$y = 4 + 2$ The opposite of -4 is 4.

$y = 6$ This is the missing y-coordinate of the solution.

The completed ordered pair is $(-4, 6)$. ∎

Self Check 3

Complete the solution
$(-3, \ \ )$ of the equation
$y = 2x - 4$.

Now Try Problem 26

3 Construct a table of solutions.

To find a solution of an equation in x and y, we can select a number, substitute it for x, and find the corresponding value of y. For example, to find a solution of the equation $y = x - 1$, we can let $x = -4$ (called the **input value**), substitute -4 for x, and solve for y (called the **output value**).

$y = x - 1$ This is the original equation.
$y = -4 - 1$ Substitute the input -4 for x.
$y = -5$ The output is -5.

$y = x - 1$		
x	y	(x, y)
-4	-5	$(-4, -5)$

The ordered pair $(-4, -5)$ is a solution. We list this ordered pair in red in the **table of solutions** (or **table of values**).

To find another solution of $y = x - 1$, we select another value of x, say -2, and find the corresponding y-value.

$y = x - 1$ This is the original equation.
$y = -2 - 1$ Substitute the input -2 for x.
$y = -3$ The output is -3.

$y = x - 1$		
x	y	(x, y)
-4	-5	$(-4, -5)$
-2	-3	$(-2, -3)$

A second solution is $(-2, -3)$, and we list it in the table of solutions.

If we let $x = 0$, we can find a third ordered pair that satisfies $y = x - 1$.

$y = x - 1$ This is the original equation.
$y = 0 - 1$ Substitute the input 0 for x.
$y = -1$ The output is -1.

$y = x - 1$		
x	y	(x, y)
-4	-5	$(-4, -5)$
-2	-3	$(-2, -3)$
0	-1	$(0, -1)$

A third solution is $(0, -1)$, which we also add to the table of solutions.

If we let $x = 2$, we can find a fourth solution.

$y = x - 1$ This is the original equation.
$y = 2 - 1$ Substitute the input 2 for x.
$y = 1$ The output is 1.

$y = x - 1$		
x	y	(x, y)
-4	-5	$(-4, -5)$
-2	-3	$(-2, -3)$
0	-1	$(0, -1)$
2	1	$(2, 1)$

A fourth solution is $(2, 1)$, and we add it to the table of solutions.

If we let $x = 4$, we have

$y = x - 1$ This is the original equation.
$y = 4 - 1$ Substitute the input 4 for x.
$y = 3$ The output is 3.

$y = x - 1$		
x	y	(x, y)
-4	-5	$(-4, -5)$
-2	-3	$(-2, -3)$
0	-1	$(0, -1)$
2	1	$(2, 1)$
4	3	$(4, 3)$

A fifth solution is $(4, 3)$.

Since we can choose any real number for x, and since any choice of x will give a corresponding value of y, it is apparent that the equation $y = x - 1$ has *infinitely many solutions*. We have found five of them: $(-4, -5)$, $(-2, -3)$, $(0, -1)$, $(2, 1)$, and $(4, 3)$.

4 Graph equations by plotting points.

To graph the equation $y = x - 1$, we plot the ordered pairs listed in the table of solutions on a rectangular coordinate system, as shown in figure (a). We can see that the five points lie on a line.

We then draw a line through the points, because the graph of any solution of $y = x - 1$ will lie on this line. The arrowheads show that the line continues forever in both directions. The line is a picture of all the solutions of the equation $y = x - 1$. This line is called the **graph of the equation.** See figure (b).

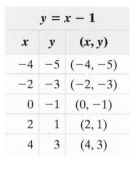

$y = x - 1$		
x	y	(x, y)
-4	-5	$(-4, -5)$
-2	-3	$(-2, -3)$
0	-1	$(0, -1)$
2	1	$(2, 1)$
4	3	$(4, 3)$

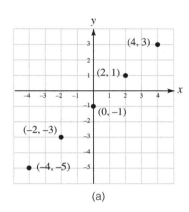

(a)

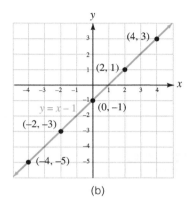

(b)

To graph an equation in x and y, we follow these steps.

Graphing an Equation in x and y

1. Make a table of solutions containing several ordered pairs of numbers (x, y) that satisfy the equation. Do this by picking values for x and finding the corresponding values for y.
2. Plot each ordered pair on a rectangular coordinate system.
3. Carefully draw a line or smooth curve through the points.

Since we will usually choose a number for x and then find the corresponding value of y, the value of y depends on x. For this reason, we call y the **dependent variable** and x the **independent variable.** The value of the independent variable is the input value, and the value of the dependent variable is the output value.

EXAMPLE 4   Graph: $y = -2x - 2$

Strategy We will find several solutions of the equation, plot them on a rectangular coordinate system, and then draw a graph passing through the points.

WHY To *graph* an equation in two variables means to make a drawing that represents all of its solutions.

Solution
To make a table of solutions, we choose numbers for x and find the corresponding values of y. If $x = -3$, we have

$y = -2x - 2$ This is the original equation.
$y = -2(-3) - 2$ Substitute -3 for x.
$y = 6 - 2$ Perform the multiplication: $-2(-3) = 6$.
$y = 4$ Perform the subtraction.

Self Check 4

Graph: $y = -3x + 1$

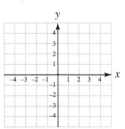

Now Try Problem 33

Thus, $x = -3$ and $y = 4$ is a solution. In a similar manner, we find the corresponding y-values for x-values of $-2, -1, 0,$ and 1 and record the results in the table of solutions. After plotting the ordered pairs, we draw a line through the points to get the graph shown.

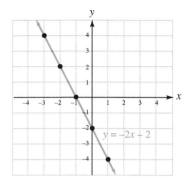

$y = -2x - 2$		
x	y	(x, y)
-3	4	$(-3, 4)$
-2	2	$(-2, 2)$
-1	0	$(-1, 0)$
0	-2	$(0, -2)$
1	-4	$(1, -4)$

As we will see in the next three examples, the graph of an equation in two variables is not always a straight line.

Self Check 5

Graph $y = x^2 - 2$ and compare the result to the graph of $y = x^2$. What do you notice?

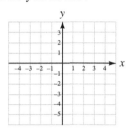

Now Try **Problem 37**

EXAMPLE 5   Graph: $y = x^2$

Strategy We will find several solutions of the equation, plot them on a rectangular coordinate system, and then draw a graph passing through the points.

WHY To *graph* an equation in two variables means to make a drawing that represents all of its solutions.

Solution
To make a table of solutions, we will choose numbers for x and find the corresponding values of y. If $x = -3$, we have

$y = x^2$ This is the original equation.

$y = (-3)^2$ Substitute the input -3 for x.

$y = 9$ The output is 9.

Thus, $x = -3$ and $y = 9$ is a solution. In a similar manner, we find the corresponding y-values for x-values of $-2, -1, 0, 1, 2,$ and 3. If we plot the ordered pairs listed in the table and join the points with a smooth curve, we get the graph shown in the figure, which is called a **parabola.**

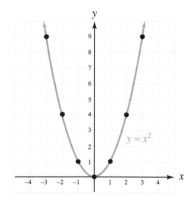

$y = x^2$		
x	y	(x, y)
-3	9	$(-3, 9)$
-2	4	$(-2, 4)$
-1	1	$(-1, 1)$
0	0	$(0, 0)$
1	1	$(1, 1)$
2	4	$(2, 4)$
3	9	$(3, 9)$

Success Tip When selecting x-values for a table of solutions, a rule of thumb is to choose some negative numbers, some positive numbers, and 0. When $x = 0$, the computations to find y are usually quite simple.

EXAMPLE 6   Graph: $y = |x|$

Strategy We will find several solutions of the equation, plot them on a rectangular coordinate system, and then draw a graph passing through the points.

WHY To *graph* an equation in two variables means to make a drawing that represents all of its solutions.

Solution
To make a table of solutions, we will choose numbers for x and find the corresponding values of y. If $x = -5$, we have

$y = |x|$ This is the original equation.
$y = |-5|$ Substitute the input -5 for x.
$y = 5$ The output is 5.

The ordered pair $(-5, 5)$ satisfies the equation. This pair and several others that satisfy the equation are listed in the table of solutions in the figure. If we plot the ordered pairs in the table, we see that they lie in a "V" shape. We join the points to complete the graph shown in the figure.

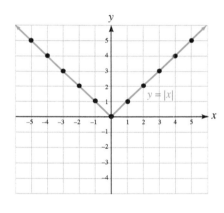

$y = |x|$		
x	y	(x, y)
-5	5	$(-5, 5)$
-4	4	$(-4, 4)$
-3	3	$(-3, 3)$
-2	2	$(-2, 2)$
-1	1	$(-1, 1)$
0	0	$(0, 0)$
1	1	$(1, 1)$
2	2	$(2, 2)$
3	3	$(3, 3)$

Self Check 6

Graph $y = |x| + 2$ and compare the result to the graph of $y = |x|$. What do you notice?

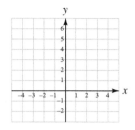

Now Try **Problem 43**

EXAMPLE 7   Graph: $y = x^3$

Strategy We will find several solutions of the equation, plot them on a rectangular coordinate system, and then draw a graph passing through the points.

WHY To *graph* an equation in two variables means to make a drawing that represents all of its solutions.

Solution
If we let $x = -2$, we have

$y = x^3$ This is the original equation.
$y = (-2)^3$ Substitute the input -2 for x.
$y = -8$ The output is -8.

The ordered pair $(-2, -8)$ satisfies the equation. This ordered pair and several others that satisfy the equation are listed in the table of solutions in the figure on the next page. Plotting the ordered pairs and joining them with a smooth curve gives us the graph shown in the figure.

Self Check 7

Graph $y = (x - 2)^3$ and compare the result to the graph of $y = x^3$. What do you notice?

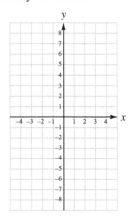

Now Try **Problem 45**

$y = x^3$		
x	y	(x, y)
-2	-8	$(-2, -8)$
-1	-1	$(-1, -1)$
0	0	$(0, 0)$
1	1	$(1, 1)$
2	8	$(2, 8)$

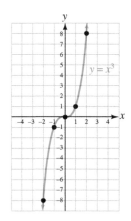

Using Your CALCULATOR   Using a Graphing Calculator to Graph an Equation

We have graphed equations by making tables of solutions and plotting points. The task of graphing is much easier when we use a graphing calculator. The instructions in this discussion will be general in nature. For specific details about your calculator, please consult your owner's manual.

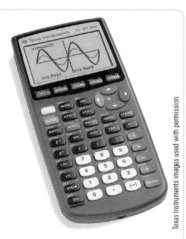

The viewing window
All graphing calculators have a viewing **window,** used to display graphs. The **standard window** has settings of

$$\text{Xmin} = -10, \quad \text{Xmax} = 10, \quad \text{Ymin} = -10, \quad \text{and} \quad \text{Ymax} = 10$$

which indicate that the minimum x- and y-coordinates used in the graph will be -10 and that the maximum x- and y-coordinates will be 10.

Graphing an equation
To graph the equation $y = x - 1$ using a graphing calculator, we press the $\boxed{\text{Y} =}$ key and enter the right-hand side of the equation after the symbol Y_1. The display will show the equation

$$Y_1 = x - 1$$

Then we press the $\boxed{\text{GRAPH}}$ key to produce the graph in figure (a) shown on the next page.

Next, we will graph the equation $y = |x - 4|$. Since absolute values are always nonnegative, the minimum y-value is zero. To obtain a reasonable viewing window, we press the $\boxed{\text{WINDOW}}$ key and set the Ymin value slightly lower, at Ymin $= -3$. We set Ymax to be 10 units greater than Ymin, at Ymax $= 7$. The minimum value of y occurs when $x = 4$. To center the graph in the viewing window, we set the Xmin and Xmax values 5 units to the left and right of 4. Therefore, Xmin $= -1$ and Xmax $= 9$.

After entering the right-hand side of the equation, we obtain the graph in figure (b) shown on the next page. Consult your owner's manual to learn how to enter an absolute value.

(continued)

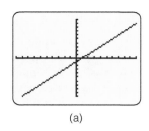

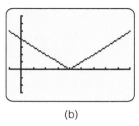

(a)   (b)

Changing the viewing window:

The choice of viewing windows is extremely important when graphing equations. To show this, let's graph $y = x^2 - 25$ with x-values from -1 to 6 and y-values from -5 to 5.

To graph this equation, we set the x and y window values and enter the right-hand side of the equation. The display will show

$$Y_1 = x^2 - 25$$

Then we press the $\boxed{\text{GRAPH}}$ key to produce the graph shown in figure (c). Although the graph appears to be a straight line, it is not. Actually, we are seeing only part of a parabola. If we pick a viewing window with x-values of -6 to 6 and y-values of -30 to 2, as in figure (d), we can see that the graph is a parabola.

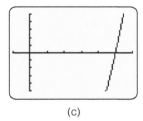

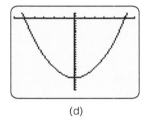

(c)   (d)

Use a graphing calculator to graph each equation. Use a viewing window of $x = -5$ to 5 and $y = -5$ to 5.

1. $y = 2.1x - 1.1$ **2.** $y = 1.12x^2 - 1$

3. $y = |x + 0.7|$ **4.** $y = 0.1x^3 + 1$

Graph each equation in a viewing window of $x = -4$ to 4 and $y = -4$ to 4. Each graph is not what it first appears to be. Pick a better viewing window and find a better representation of the true graph.

5. $y = -x^3 - 8.2$ **6.** $y = -|x - 4.01|$

7. $y = x^2 + 5.9$ **8.** $y = -x + 7.95$

5 Graph equations that use different variables.

We will often encounter equations with variables other than x and y. When we make tables of solutions and graph these equations, we must know which is the independent variable (the input values) and which is the dependent variable (the output values). The independent variable is usually associated with the horizontal axis of the coordinate system, and the dependent variable is usually associated with the vertical axis.

Self Check 8

SPEED LIMITS If the maximum speed limit on a rural highway is 55 mph, the formula for the distance traveled in t time is $d = 55t$. Graph the equation.

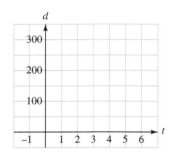

Now Try **Problem 57**

EXAMPLE 8   *Speed Limits*   In some states, the maximum speed limit on a U.S. interstate highway is 75 mph. The distance covered by a vehicle traveling at 75 mph depends on the time the vehicle travels at that speed. This relationship is described by the equation $d = 75t$, where d represents the distance (in miles) and t represents the time (in hours). Graph the equation.

Strategy We will find several solutions of the equation, plot them on a rectangular coordinate system, and then draw a graph passing through the points.

WHY We can use the graph to estimate the distance traveled (in miles) after traveling an amount of time at 75 mph.

Solution
Since d depends on t in the equation $d = 75t$, t is the independent variable (the input) and d is the dependent variable (the output). Therefore, we choose values for t and find the corresponding values of d. Since t represents the time spent traveling at 75 mph, we choose no negative values for t.
    If $t = 0$, we have

$$d = 75t \qquad \text{This is the original equation.}$$
$$d = 75(0) \qquad \text{Substitute the input 0 for } t.$$
$$d = 0 \qquad \text{Perform the multiplication.}$$

The pair $t = 0$ and $d = 0$, or $(0, 0)$, is a solution. This ordered pair and others that satisfy the equation are listed in the table of solutions shown below. If we plot the ordered pairs and draw a line through them, we obtain the graph shown in the figure. From the graph, we see (as expected) that the distance covered steadily increases as the traveling time increases.

$d = 75t$		
t	d	(t, d)
0	0	$(0, 0)$
1	75	$(1, 75)$
2	150	$(2, 150)$
3	225	$(3, 225)$
4	300	$(4, 300)$
5	375	$(5, 375)$

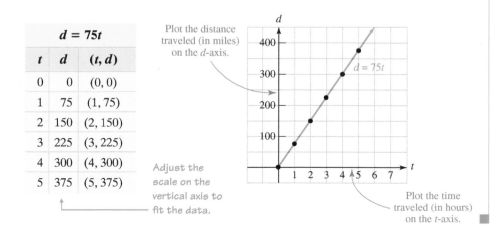

ANSWERS TO SELF CHECKS

1. yes **2.** no **3.** $(-3, -10)$

4.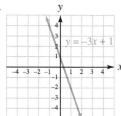

5.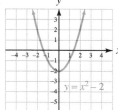

6.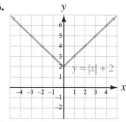

7.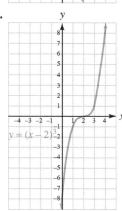

8.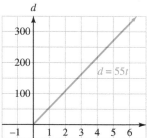

SECTION 5.3 STUDY SET

VOCABULARY

Fill in the blanks.

1. The equation $7 = -2x + 5$ is an equation in _____ variable. The equation $y = x + 1$ is an equation in _____ variables, x and y.

2. An ordered pair is a _____ of an equation if the numbers in the ordered pair satisfy the equation.

3. When constructing a _____ of solutions, the values of x are the input values and the values of y are the _____ values.

4. In equations containing the variables x and y, x is called the independent _____ and y is called the _____ variable.

CONCEPTS

5. Consider the equation: $y = -2x + 6$

   a. How many variables does the equation contain?

   b. Does the ordered pair $(4, -2)$ satisfy the equation?

   c. Is $(-3, 12)$ a solution of the equation?

   d. How many solutions does this equation have?

6. To graph an equation, five solutions were found, they were plotted (in black), and a straight line was drawn through them, as shown. From the graph, determine three other solutions of the equation.

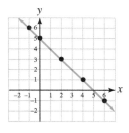

7. Fill in the blanks: The graph of $y = -x + 5$ is shown in Problem 6. Every point on the graph represents an ordered-pair _____ of $y = -x + 5$, and every ordered-pair solution is a _____ on the graph.

8. Consider the graph of an equation shown below.

   a. If the coordinates of point M are substituted into the equation, is the result a true or false statement?

   b. If the coordinates of point N are substituted into the equation, is the result a true or false statement?

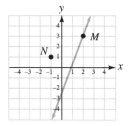

9. Complete the table.

$y = x^3$	
x (inputs)	**y (outputs)**
0	
−1	
−2	
1	
2	

10. What is wrong with the graph of $y = x − 3$ shown on the right?

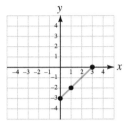

11. To graph $y = −x + 1$, a student constructed a table of solutions and plotted the ordered pairs as shown. Instead of drawing a crooked line through the points, what should he have done?

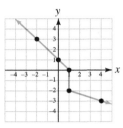

12. To graph $y = x^2 − 4$, a table of solutions is constructed and a graph is drawn, as shown. Explain the error made here.

$y = x^2 − 4$		
x	**y**	**(x, y)**
0	−4	(0, −4)
2	0	(2, 0)

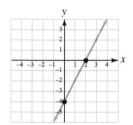

13. Explain the error with the graph of $y = x^2$ shown in the illustration.

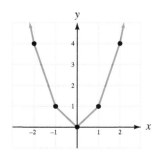

14. Several solutions of an equation are listed in the table of solutions. When graphing them, with what variable should the horizontal and vertical axes of the graph be labeled?

t	s	(t, s)
0	4	(0, 4)
1	5	(1, 5)
2	10	(2, 10)

NOTATION

Complete each step.

15. Verify that $(−2, 6)$ satisfies $y = −x + 4$.

$$y = −x + 4$$
$$\boxed{} \overset{?}{=} −\left(\boxed{}\right) + 4$$
$$6 \overset{?}{=} \boxed{} + 4$$
$$6 = 6$$

16. For the equation $y = |x − 2|$, if $x = −3$, find y.

$$y = |x − 2|$$
$$y = \left|\boxed{} − 2\right|$$
$$y = \left|\boxed{}\right|$$
$$y = 5$$

GUIDED PRACTICE

Determine whether the ordered pair satisfies the equation.
See Examples 1–2.

17. $y = 2x − 4, (4, 4)$ **18.** $y = −3x + 1, (2, −4)$

19. $y = x^2, (8, 48)$ **20.** $y = −x^2 + 2, (1, 1)$

21. $y = |x − 2|, (4, −3)$ **22.** $y = |x + 3|, (0, 3)$

23. $y = x^3 + 1, (−2, −7)$ **24.** $y = −x^3 − 1, (1, −2)$

Complete the solution of each equation. See Example 3.

25. $y = 3x − 4, (1, ?)$

26. $y = \dfrac{1}{2}x − 3, (2, ?)$

27. $y = −5x + 3, (−3, ?)$

28. $y = −\dfrac{2}{5}x − 1, (−5, ?)$

Complete each table. See Objective 3.

29.

$y = x − 3$	
x	**y**
0	
1	
−2	

30.

$y = |x − 3|$	
x	**y**
0	
−1	
3	

31.

$y = x^2 - 3$	
Input	Output
0	
2	
−2	

32.

$y = x + 1$	
Input	Output
0	
2	
−1	

Construct a table of solutions and graph each equation.
Compare the result to the graph of $y = |x|$. See Example 6.

41. $y = -|x|$

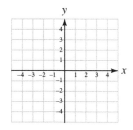

42. $y = |x| - 2$

43. $y = |x + 2|$

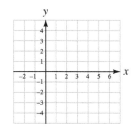

44. $y = |x - 2|$

Construct a table of solutions and graph each equation.
See Example 4.

33. $y = 2x - 3$

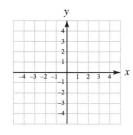

34. $y = 3x + 1$

35. $y = -2x + 1$

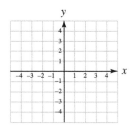

36. $y = -3x + 2$

Construct a table of solutions and graph each equation.
Compare the result to the graph of $y = x^2$. See Example 5.

37. $y = x^2 + 1$

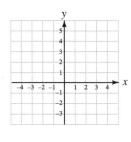

38. $y = -x^2$

39. $y = (x - 2)^2$

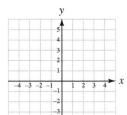

40. $y = (x + 2)^2$

Construct a table of solutions and graph each equation.
Compare the result to the graph of $y = x^3$. See Example 7.

45. $y = -x^3$

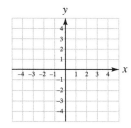

46. $y = x^3 + 2$

47. $y = x^3 - 2$

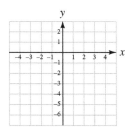

48. $y = (x + 2)^3$

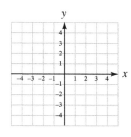
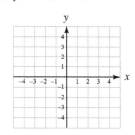
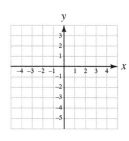
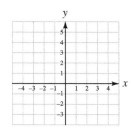
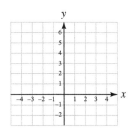
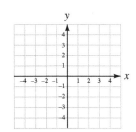
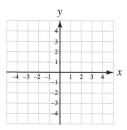
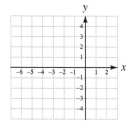

CONCEPT EXTENSION

49. TIRE WEAR Refer to the graph below. At what percent(s) of inflation will a tire offer only 90% of its possible service?

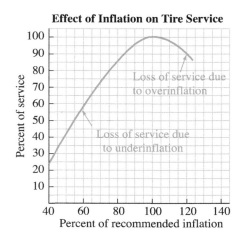

Effect of Inflation on Tire Service

50. SATELLITE ANTENNAS The cross section of the satellite antenna in the illustration is a parabola given by the equation $y = \frac{1}{16}x^2$, with distances measured in feet. If the dish is 8 feet wide, how deep is it?

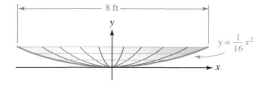

APPLICATIONS

See Example 8.

51. BILLIARDS The path traveled by the black 8 ball is described by the equations $y = 2x - 4$ and $y = -2x + 12$. Construct a table of solutions for $y = 2x - 4$ using the x-values 1, 2, and 4. Do the same for $y = -2x + 12$ using the x-values 4, 6, and 8. Then graph the path of the 8 ball.

x	1	2	4	4	6	8
y						

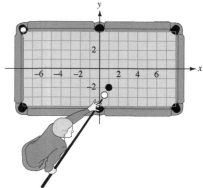

52. TABLE TENNIS The illustration shows the path traveled by a Ping-Pong ball as it bounces off the table. Use the information in the illustration to complete the table.

x	-7	-3	1	3	5
y					

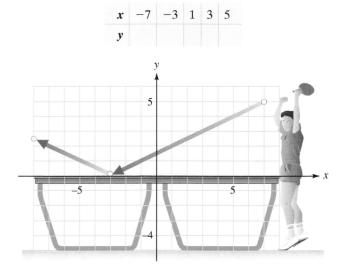

53. SUSPENSION BRIDGES The suspension cables of a bridge hang in the shape of a parabola, as shown below. Use the information in the illustration to complete the table.

x	0	2	4	-2	-4
y					

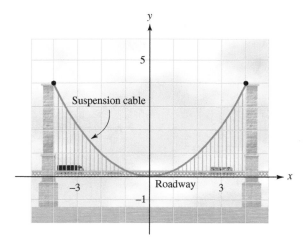

54. FIRE BOATS A stream of water from a high-pressure hose on a fire boat travels in the shape of a parabola. Use the information in the graph on the next page to complete the table.

x	1	2	3	4
y				

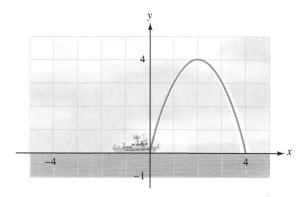

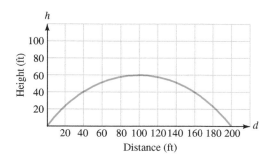

55. MANUFACTURING The following graph shows the relationship between the length *l* (in inches) of a machine bolt and the cost *C* (in cents) to manufacture it.

  a. What information does the point (2, 8) on the graph give us?

  b. How much does it cost to make a 7-inch bolt?

  c. What length bolt is the least expensive to make?

  d. Describe how the cost changes as the length of the bolt increases.

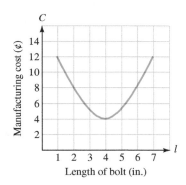

56. SOFTBALL The graph in the next column shows the relationship between the distance *d* (in feet) traveled by a batted softball and the height *h* (in feet) it attains.

  a. What information does the point (40, 40) on the graph give us?

  b. At what distance from home plate does the ball reach its maximum height?

  c. Where will the ball land?

57. MARKET VALUE OF A HOUSE The following graph shows the relationship between the market value *v* of a house and the time *t* since it was purchased.

  a. What was the purchase price of the house?

  b. When did the value of the house reach its lowest point?

  c. When did the value of the house begin to surpass the purchase price?

  d. Describe how the market value of the house changed over the 8-year period.

58. POLITICAL SURVEYS The graph on the next page shows the relationship between the percent *P* of those surveyed who rated their senator's job performance as satisfactory or better and the time *t* she had been in office.

  a. When did her job performance rating reach a maximum?

  b. When was her job performance rating at or above the 60% mark?

  c. Describe how her job performance rating changed over the 12-month period.

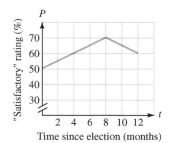

Time since election (months)

59. OPTICS See the illustration. The **law of reflection** states that the angle of reflection is equal to the angle of incidence. What function studied in this section models the path of the reflected light beam with an angle of incidence measuring 45°?

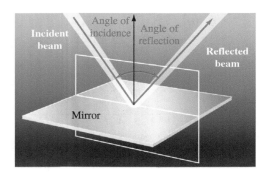

60. CENTER OF GRAVITY See the illustration. As a diver performs a $1\frac{1}{2}$-somersault in the tuck position, her center of gravity follows a path that can be described by a graph shape studied in this section. What graph shape is that?

WRITING

61. What is a table of solutions?

62. To graph an equation in two variables, how many solutions of the equation must be found?

63. Give an example of an equation in one variable and an equation in two variables. How do their solutions differ?

64. When we say that $(-2, -6)$ is a solution of $y = x - 4$, what do we mean?

65. On a quiz, students were asked to graph $y = 3x - 1$. One student made the table of solutions on the left. Another student made the one on the right. Which table is incorrect? Or could they both be correct? Explain.

x	y	(x, y)
0	−1	(0, −1)
2	5	(2, 5)
3	8	(3, 8)
4	11	(4, 11)
5	14	(5, 14)

x	y	(x, y)
−2	−7	(−2, −7)
−1	−4	(−1, −4)
1	2	(1, 2)
−3	−10	(−3, −10)
2	5	(2, 5)

66. What does it mean when we say that an equation in two variables has infinitely many solutions?

67. Describe the graph of an absolute value equation in two variables.

68. What is a parabola?

SECTION 5.4
Applications Introduction Linear Models

In Section 5.3, we studied a method for graphing equations in two variables. Recall that the graphs of two of the equations discussed in that section, $y = x - 1$ and $y = -2x - 2$, were straight lines. Equations like these are called **linear equations**.

   Linear equations can be used to model many real-life situations. **Linear models**, as they are called, often are written in variables other than x and y. As a result, we must make the appropriate changes when labeling the table of solutions and the graph of the equation. We can use linear models to make observations about what has occurred in the past and make predictions about what might occur in the future.

1. FARMERS MARKETS The increasing popularity of farmers markets in the United States can be modeled by the linear equation $f = 265t + 2{,}728$, where t represents the number of years after 2000 and f represents the number of farmers markets. (*Source:* U.S. Department of Agriculture)

   a. To find the number of farmers markets in the year 2000 (which is 0 years after 2000), evaluate $265t + 2{,}728$ for $t = 0$.

   b. To find the number of farmers markets in the year 2002 (which is 2 years after 2000), evaluate $265t + 2{,}728$ for $t = 2$.

   c. To find the number of farmers markets in the year 2005 (which is 5 years after 2000), evaluate $265t + 2{,}728$ for $t = 5$.

   d. Use your results from parts a, b, and c to complete the table of solutions below.

t	f	(t, f)
0		
2		
5		

   e. Plot the ordered pairs listed in the table on the coordinate system on the next page. Then draw a straight line through them.

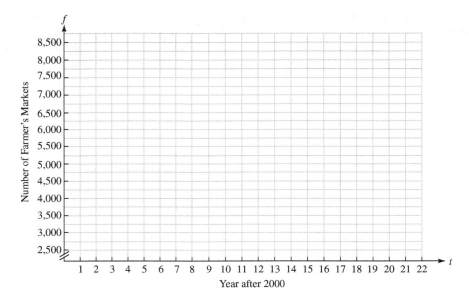

f. Suppose the trend in the growth of farmers markets continues. Use your graph to predict the approximate number of famers markets in the year 2020.

2. CLEANING WINDOWS The linear equation $A = -0.03n + 32$ estimates the amount A of glass-cleaning solution (in ounces) that is left in the bottle after the sprayer trigger has been pulled a total of n times.

a. Complete the table of solutions below. Since any value of n is to be multiplied by a decimal, selecting powers of 10 makes the computations to find A simpler.

n	A	(n, A)
0		
100		
1,000		

b. Plot the ordered pairs listed in the table on the coordinate system below. Then draw a straight line through them.

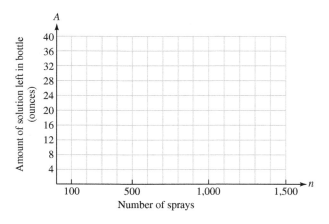

c. Use your graph to estimate the amount of solution that is left in the bottle after 800 sprays.

3. NFL TICKETS The average ticket price p to a National Football League game is approximated by the linear model $p = 2.7t + 20$, where t is the number of years after 1990. (*Source:* Team Marketing Report, NFL.)

   a. Construct a table of solutions. Select values of t that correspond to the years 1990, 2000, and 2010.

t	p	(t, p)

   b. Plot the ordered pairs listed in the table on a coordinate system. Scale the t-axis in units of 2 years and the p-axis in units of $10. Then draw a straight line through them.

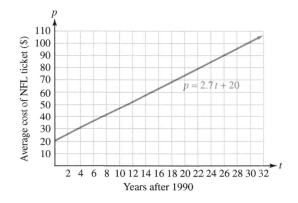

   c. Use the graph to predict the average ticket price in 2020 if the current trend continues.

4. SHARPENING PENCILS The linear equation $L = -0.04t + 8$ estimates the length L (in inches) of a pencil after it has been inserted into a sharpener and the handle turned a total of t times.

   a. Construct a table of solutions.

t	L	(t, L)

b. Plot the ordered pairs listed in the table on a coordinate system. Scale the *t*-axis in units of 10 turns and the *L*-axis in units of 1 inch. Then draw a straight line through them.

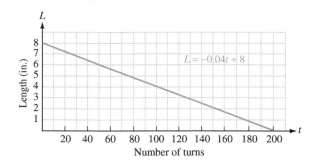

c. Use the graph to estimate the length of the pencil after 75 turns of the handle.

5. OWNING A CAR In 2010, the average cost *c* (in dollars) to own and operate a car was estimated by the linear model $c = 0.57m$, where *m* represents the number of miles driven. (*Source*: AAA Auto Club)

a. Complete the table of solutions.

m	*c*	*(m, c)*
0		
10,000		
20,000		

b. Plot the ordered pairs listed in the table on a coordinate system. Then draw a straight line through them. Scale the *m*-axis in units of 2,500 miles and the *c*-axis in units of $2,000.

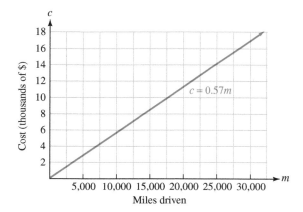

c. Use the graph to estimate the cost in 2010 of operating a car that is driven 30,000 miles.

6. U.S. SPACE PROGRAM Since 1980, the Gallup Poll organization has surveyed Americans to see whether they think the space program has brought enough benefits to the country to justify its cost. The percent *p* responding "yes" is estimated by the

linear model $p = \frac{3}{5}t + 40$, where t is the number of years after 1980.
(*Source*: galluppoll.com)

a. Construct a table of solutions. Select values of *t* that correspond to the years 1980, 1990, and 2000.

t	*p*	(*t, p*)

b. Plot the ordered pairs listed in the table on a coordinate system. Then draw a straight line through them. Scale the *t*-axis in units of 5 years and the *p*-axis in units of 10%.

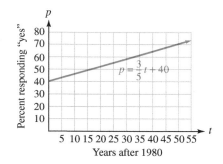

c. If the polling trend continues, when will the percent that respond "yes" reach 70%?

SECTION 5.4
Graphing Linear Equations

Objectives

1 Identify linear equations.

2 Graph linear equations by plotting points.

3 Write and graph linear equation models.

4 Graph linear equations by the intercept method.

5 Obtain information from intercepts.

6 Identify and graph horizontal and vertical lines.

ARE YOU READY?

The following problems review some basic skills that are needed when graphing ordered pairs.

1. Evaluate $-6x - 7$ for $x = -2$.

2. Solve for *y*: $4x + 5y = -15$

3. Multiply: $\frac{3}{2}(2)$

4. Multiply: $-\frac{5}{9}(-9)$

5. Graph the points $(2, 0)$, $(-4, 0)$, $(0, 1)$ and $(0, -3)$.

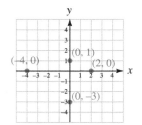

6. What is the *x*-coordinate of any point that lies on the *y*-axis?

7. What point lies on both the *x*-axis and the *y*-axis?

8. Solve: $3(0) + 2y = 10$

1 **Identify linear equations.**

In section 5.3, we graphed the equations in two variables shown below.

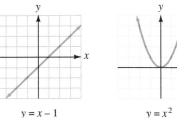

$$y = x - 1 \qquad y = x^2$$

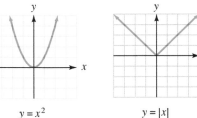

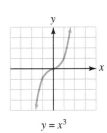

$$y = |x| \qquad y = x^3$$

The equation $y = x - 1$ is said to be *linear* and its graph is a line. By definition, a linear equation in two variables is any equation that can be written in the following form, where the variable terms appear on one side of an equal symbol and a constant appears on the other.

Linear Equations

A linear equation in two variables is an equation that can be written in the form

$$Ax + By = C$$

where A, B, and C are real numbers and A and B are not both 0. This form is called standard form.*

*In some textbooks, the definition of the standard form of a linear equation in two variables contains additional requirements, such as: A, B, and C are integers, $A > 0$, and the greatest common factor of A, B, and C is 1.

Every linear equation in two variables has an infinite number of ordered-pair solutions. The graph of a linear equation in two variables is a straight line. Every point on the line corresponds to a solution.

Some more examples of linear equations are

$$y = 2x + 4, \qquad 2x + 3y = 12, \qquad \text{and} \qquad 3x = 5y$$

The exponent on each variable of a linear equation in two variables is an understood 1. For example, $y = 2x + 4$ can be thought of as $y^1 = 2x^1 + 4$ and $2x + 3y = 12$ can be thought of as $2x^1 + 3y^1 = 12$.

Some of the equations that we graphed in Section 5.3 are *not* linear equations.

$y = x^2$ This is not a linear equation because x is squared.

$y = |x|$ This is not a linear equation because of the absolute value.

$y = x^3$ This is not a linear equation because x is cubed.

Some more examples of equations in two variables that are *not* linear are shown below. You will see in other modules and in more advanced courses that the graphs of these equations are not straight lines.

$$y = x^2 + 3, \qquad y = \sqrt{x}, \qquad y = 4^x, \qquad x^2 + y^2 = 25, \qquad \text{and} \qquad y = \frac{1}{x}$$

2 Graph linear equations by plotting points.

Linear equations can be graphed in several ways. Generally, the form in which an equation is written determines the method that we use to graph it. To graph linear equations solved for y, such as $y = 2x + 4$, we can use the following **point-plotting method.**

Graphing Linear Equations Solved for *y* by Plotting Points

1. Find three ordered pairs that are solutions of the equation by selecting three values for x and calculating the corresponding values of y.

2. Plot the solutions on a rectangular coordinate system.

3. Draw a straight line passing through the points. If the points do not lie on a line, check your calculations.

Success Tip   When selecting x-values for a table of solutions, a rule of thumb is to choose a negative number, a positive number, and 0. When $x = 0$, the calculations to find y are usually quite simple.

EXAMPLE 1   Graph: $y = 2x + 4$

Strategy We will find three solutions of the equation, plot them on a rectangular coordinate system, and then draw a straight line passing through the points.

WHY To *graph* a linear equation in two variables means to make a drawing that represents all of its solutions.

Solution
To find three solutions of this linear equation, we select three values for x that will make the calculations easy. Then we find each corresponding value of y.

If x = −2:	*If x = 0:*	*If x = 2:*
$y = 2x + 4$	$y = 2x + 4$	$y = 2x + 4$
$y = 2(-2) + 4$	$y = 2(0) + 4$	$y = 2(2) + 4$
$y = -4 + 4$	$y = 0 + 4$	$y = 4 + 4$
$y = 0$	$y = 4$	$y = 8$
$(-2, 0)$ is a solution	$(0, 4)$ is a solution.	$(2, 8)$ is a solution.

We enter the results in a table of solutions and plot the ordered pairs. Then we draw a straight line through the points and label it $y = 2x + 4$.

$y = 2x + 4$

x	*y*	*(x, y)*
−2	0	$(-2, 0)$
0	4	$(0, 4)$
2	8	$(2, 8)$
↑	↑	↑
Select	Find	Plot

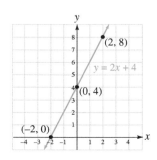

Self Check 1

Graph : $y = 2x - 2$

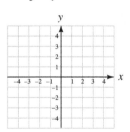

Now Try **Problem 29**

As a check, we can pick two points that the line appears to pass through, such as $(1, 6)$ and $(-1, 2)$. When we substitute their coordinates into the given equation, the two true statements that result indicate that $(1, 6)$ and $(-1, 2)$ are solutions and that the graph of the line is correctly drawn.

Check $(1, 6)$: $y = 2x + 4$ **Check $(-1, 2)$:** $y = 2x + 4$

$\qquad\qquad\qquad 6 \overset{2}{=} 2(1) + 4$ $\qquad\qquad\qquad\qquad\qquad 2 \overset{2}{=} 2(-1) + 4$

$\qquad\qquad\qquad 6 \overset{2}{=} 2 + 4$ $\qquad\qquad\qquad\qquad\qquad\quad 2 \overset{2}{=} -2 + 4$

$\qquad\qquad\qquad 6 = 6$ True $\qquad\qquad\qquad\qquad\quad 2 = 2$ True

---

Success Tip   Since two points determine a line, only two points are needed to graph a linear equation. However, we will often plot a third point as a check. If the three points do not lie on a straight line, then at least one of them is in error.

To graph linear equations in x and y using the point plotting method of this section, the variable y must be isolated on one side of the equation.

Self Check 2

Solve $3y = 3 + x$ for y. Then graph the equation.

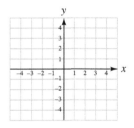

Now Try Problem 39

EXAMPLE 2   Graph: $2y = 4 - x$

Strategy We will use properties of equality to solve the given equation for y. Then we will use the point-plotting method of this section to graph the resulting equivalent equation.

WHY The calculations to find several solutions of a linear equation in two variables are usually easier when the equation is solved for y.

Solution
To solve for y, we undo the multiplication of 2 by dividing both sides by 2.

$$2y = 4 - x$$

$$\frac{2y}{2} = \frac{4}{2} - \frac{x}{2} \qquad \text{On the right-hand side, dividing each term by 2 is equivalent to dividing the entire side by 2: } \frac{4-x}{2} = \frac{4}{2} - \frac{x}{2}.$$

$$y = 2 - \frac{x}{2} \qquad \text{Simplify: } \frac{4}{2} = 2$$

Since each value of x will be divided by 2, we will choose values of x that are divisible by 2. Three such choices are -4, 0, and 4. If $x = -4$, we have

$$y = 2 - \frac{x}{2}$$

$$y = 2 - \frac{-4}{2} \qquad \text{Substitute } -4 \text{ for } x.$$

$$y = 2 - (-2) \quad \text{Divide: } \frac{-4}{2} = -2$$

$$y = 4 \qquad\qquad \text{Perform the subtraction.}$$

A solution is $(-4, 4)$. This pair and two others satisfying the equation are shown in the table on the next page. If we plot the ordered pairs and draw a straight line through the points, we will obtain the graph also shown on the next page.

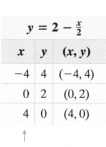

$$y = 2 - \frac{x}{2}$$

x	y	(x, y)
-4	4	$(-4, 4)$
0	2	$(0, 2)$
4	0	$(4, 0)$

Select values that are divisible by 2.

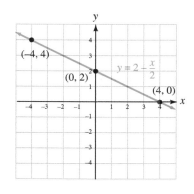

3 Write and graph linear equation models.

Linear equations can be used to model many real-life situations. **Linear models**, as they are called, often are written in variables other than x and y. As a result, we must make the appropriate changes when labeling the table of solutions and the graph of the equation. We can use linear models to make observations about what has occurred in the past and make predictions about what might occur in the future.

EXAMPLE 3   *Birthday Parties*   A restaurant offers a party package that includes food, drinks, cake, and party favors for a cost of $25 plus $3 per child. Write a linear equation that will give the cost for a party of any size, and then graph the equation.

Strategy We will form an equation (a linear model) and use the point-plotting method to graph the equation.

WHY The graph is a picture of all the solutions of the equation.

Solution
We can let c represent the cost of the party. The cost c is the sum of the basic charge of $25 and the cost per child times the number of children attending. If the number of children attending is n, at $3 per child, the total cost for the children is $3n$.

The cost	is	the basic $25 charge	plus	$3	times	the number of children.
c	$=$	25	$+$	3	$\cdot$	n

For the equation $c = 25 + 3n$, the independent variable (input) is n, the number of children. The dependent variable (output) is c, the cost of the party. We will find three points on the graph of the equation by choosing n-values of 0, 5, and 10 and finding the corresponding c-values. The results are shown in the table.

If $n = 0$	If $n = 5$	If $n = 10$
$c = 25 + 3(0)$	$c = 25 + 3(5)$	$c = 25 + 3(10)$
$c = 25$	$c = 25 + 15$	$c = 25 + 30$
	$c = 40$	$c = 55$

$c = 25 + 3n$		
n	c	(n, c)
0	25	$(0, 25)$
5	40	$(5, 40)$
10	55	$(10, 55)$

Self Check 3

PARTY PACKAGES A laser tag business offers a package that includes invitations, a party room, and 2 rounds of laser tag. The cost is $15 plus $10 per child. Write a linear equation that will give the cost for a party of any size, and then graph the equation.

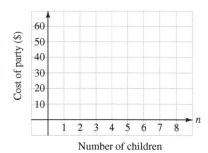

Number of children

Now Try Problem 83

Next, we graph the ordered pairs in the table and draw a line through the points. We don't draw an arrowhead on the left, because it doesn't make sense to have a negative number of children attend a party. Note that the c-axis is scaled in units of \$5 to accommodate costs ranging from \$0 to \$65. We can use the graph to determine the cost of a party of any size. For example, to find the cost of a party with 8 children, we locate 8 on the horizontal axis and then move up to find a point on the graph directly above the 8. Since the coordinates of that point are $(8, 49)$, the cost for 8 children would be \$49.

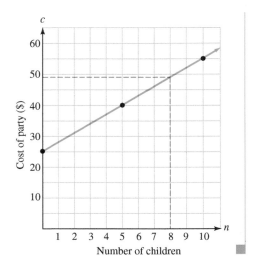

The graph of $y = 2x - 4$ is shown below. We see that the graph intersects (crosses) the y-axis at the point $(0, -4)$; this point is called the **y-intercept** of the graph. The graph intersects (crosses) the x-axis at the point $(2, 0)$; this point is called the **x-intercept** of the graph.

The Language of Algebra

Note the difference in spelling. The point where a line **intersects** the x- or y-axis is called an intercept.

Recall that the x-coordinate of any point on the y-axis is 0.

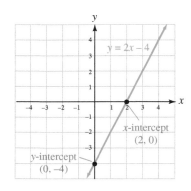

Recall that the y-coordinate of any point on the x-axis is 0.

In this example, we see that the y-intercept of the graph has an x-coordinate of 0, and the x-intercept has a y-coordinate of 0. These observations suggest the following procedures for finding the intercepts of a graph from its equation.

Finding Intercepts

To find the y-intercept, substitute 0 for x in the given equation and solve for y.
To find the x-intercept, substitute 0 for y in the given equation and solve for x.

Plotting the x- and y-intercepts of a graph and drawing a straight line through them is called the **intercept method of graphing a line.** This method is useful when graphing equations written in general form $Ax + By = C$.

EXAMPLE 4   Graph: $3x - 2y = 8$

Strategy We will let $y = 0$ to find the x-intercept of the graph. We will then let $x = 0$ to find the y-intercept.

WHY Since two points determine a line, the y-intercept and the x-intercept are enough information to graph this linear equation.

Solution
***x*-intercept: $y = 0$**

$$3x - 2y = 8$$
$$3x - 2(0) = 8 \quad \text{Substitute 0 for y.}$$
$$3x = 8 \quad \text{Simplify the left-hand side: 2(0) = 0.}$$
$$x = \frac{8}{3} \quad \text{Divide both sides by 3.}$$

The x-intercept is $\left(\frac{8}{3}, 0\right)$, which can be written $\left(2\frac{2}{3}, 0\right)$. This ordered pair is entered in the table below.

***y*-intercept: $x = 0$.**

$$3x - 2y = 8$$
$$3(0) - 2y = 8 \quad \text{Substitute 0 for x.}$$
$$-2y = 8 \quad \text{Simplify the left-hand side: 3(0) = 0.}$$
$$y = -4 \quad \text{Divide both sides by -2.}$$

The y-intercept is $(0, -4)$. It is entered in the table below. As a check, we find one more point on the line. If $x = 4$, then $y = 2$. We plot these three points and draw a straight line through them. The graph of $3x - 2y = 8$ is shown in the figure.

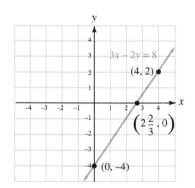

$3x - 2y = 8$		
x	y	(x, y)
$\frac{8}{3} = 2\frac{2}{3}$	0	$\left(2\frac{2}{3}, 0\right)$
0	-4	$(0, -4)$
4	2	$(4, 2)$

↑
This point serves
as a check.

Self Check 4

Graph $4x + 3y = 6$ using the intercept method.

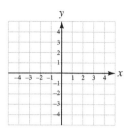

Now Try **Problem 49**

EXAMPLE 5   Graph $2x + 3y = 0$ by finding the intercepts.

Strategy We will let $x = 0$ to find the y-intercept of the graph. We will then let $y = 0$ to find the x-intercept.

WHY Since two points determine a line, the y-intercept and x-intercept are enough information to graph this linear equation.

Solution
When we find the y- and x-intercepts we see that they are both $(0, 0)$. In this case, the line passes through the origin. Since we are using two points and a check point to graph lines, we need to find two more ordered-pair solutions.

Self Check 5

Graph: $5x - 2y = 0$ by finding the intercepts.

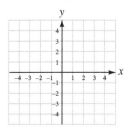

If $x = 3$, we see that $(3, -2)$ is a solution. And if $x = -3$, we see that $(-3, 2)$ is also a solution. These two solutions and the origin are plotted and a straight line is drawn through them to give the graph of $2x + 3y = 0$.

y-intercept: Let x = 0	*x-intercept: Let y = 0*	*Let x = 3*	*Let x = -3*
$2x + 3y = 0$	$2x + 3y = 0$	$2x + 3y = 0$	$2x + 3y = 0$
$2(0) + 3y = 0$	$2x + 3(0) = 0$	$2(3) + 3y = 0$	$2(-3) + 3y = 0$
$3y = 0$	$2x = 0$	$6 + 3y = 0$	$-6 + 3y = 0$
$y = 0$	$x = 0$	$3y = -6$	$3y = 6$
The *y*-intercept is $(0, 0)$.	The *x*-intercept is $(0, 0)$.	$y = -2$	$y = 2$
		$(3, -2)$ is a solution.	$(-3, 2)$ is a solution.

The intercepts are the same.

Now Try **Problem 53**

$2x + 3y = 0$		
x	y	(x, y)
0	0	$(0, 0)$	← The x-intercept and y-intercept.
3	-2	$(3, -2)$	← A solution.
-3	2	$(-3, 2)$	← This solution serves as a check point.

Equations that can be written in the form $Ax + By = 0$, such as $2x + 3y = 0$, have graphs that pass through the origin. To find another point on such a line that has integer coordinates, select an x-value equal to the coefficient of y or the opposite of the coefficient of y. Then substitute that x-value into the equation and solve for y.

5 Obtain Information from Intercepts.

The ability to read and interpret graphs is a valuable skill. When analyzing a graph, we should locate and examine the intercepts. As the following example illustrates, the coordinates of the intercepts can give useful information.

EXAMPLE 6   *Hybrid Mileage*   Figure (a) shows mileage data for a 2010 Toyota Prius Hybrid. What information do the intercepts give about the car?

©Michael Doolittle/Alamy

Now Try **Problems 83 and 84**

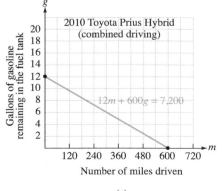

(a)

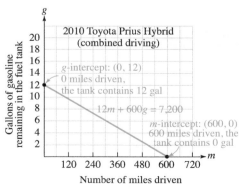

(b)

Strategy We will determine where the graph (the line in red) intersects the g-axis and where it intersects the m-axis.

WHY Once we know the intercepts, we can interpret their meaning.

Solution
See figure (b). The g-intercept $(0, 12)$ indicates that when the car has been driven 0 miles, the fuel tank contains 12 gallons of gasoline. That is, the Prius has a 12-gallon fuel tank.

The m-intercept $(600, 0)$ indicates that after 600 miles of combined driving, the fuel tank contains 0 gallons of gasoline. Thus, 600 miles of combined driving can be done on 1 tank of gas in a Prius.

6 Identify and graph horizontal and vertical lines.

Equations such as $y = 4$ and $x = -3$ are linear equations, because they can be written in the general form $Ax + By = C$. For example, $y = 4$ is equivalent to $0x + 1y = 4$ and $x = -3$ is equivalent to $1x + 0y = -3$. We now discuss how to graph these types of linear equations.

EXAMPLE 7   Graph: $y = 4$

Strategy To find three ordered-pair solutions of this equation to plot, we will select three values for x and use 4 for y each time.

WHY The given equation requires that $y = 4$.

Solution
We can write the equation in general form as $0x + y = 4$. Since the coefficient of x is 0, the numbers chosen for x have no effect on y. The value of y is always 4. For example, if $x = 2$, we have

$$0x + y = 4 \quad \text{This is the original equation, } y = 4, \text{ written in general form.}$$
$$0(2) + y = 4 \quad \text{Substitute 2 for } x.$$
$$y = 4 \quad \text{Simplify the left side.}$$

The table of solutions shown below contains three ordered pairs that satisfy the equation $y = 4$. If we plot the points and draw a straight line through them, the result is a horizontal line. The y-intercept is $(0, 4)$, and there is no x-intercept.

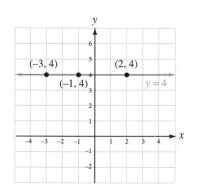

$y = 4$		
x	y	(x, y)
2	4	$(2, 4)$
-1	4	$(-1, 4)$
-3	4	$(-3, 4)$

↑
Note that each
y-coordinate is 4.

Self Check 7
Graph: $y = -2$

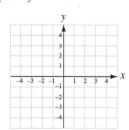

Now Try Problem 57

Self Check 8

Graph: $x = 4$

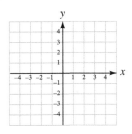

Now Try Problem 59

EXAMPLE 8 Graph: $x = -3$

Strategy To find three ordered-pair solutions of this equation to plot, we will select -3 for x each time and use three different values for y.

WHY The given equation requires that $x = -3$.

Solution

We can write the equation in general form as $x + 0y = -3$. Since the coefficient of y is 0, the numbers chosen for y have no effect on x. The value of x is always -3. For example, if $y = -2$, we have

$$x + 0y = -3 \qquad \text{This is the original equation written in general form.}$$
$$x + 0(-2) = -3 \qquad \text{Substitute } -2 \text{ for } y.$$
$$x = -3 \qquad \text{Simplify the left side.}$$

The table of solutions shown below contains three ordered pairs that satisfy the equation $x = -3$. If we plot the points and draw a line through them, the result is a vertical line. The x-intercept is $(-3, 0)$, and there is no y-intercept.

$x = -3$		
x	y	(x, y)
-3	-2	$(-3, -2)$
-3	0	$(-3, 0)$
-3	3	$(-3, 3)$

↑
Note that each
x-coordinate is −3.

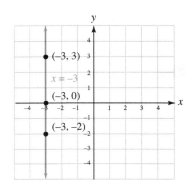

From the results of Examples 7 and 8, we have the following facts.

Equations of Horizontal and Vertical Lines

The graph of $y = b$ is a horizontal line with y-intercept $(0, b)$.

The graph of $x = a$ is a vertical line with x-intercept $(a, 0)$.

The graph of $y = 0$ is the x-axis. The graph of $x = 0$ is the y-axis.

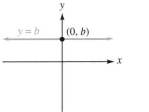

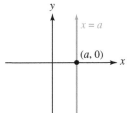

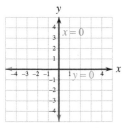

ANSWERS TO SELF CHECKS

1.
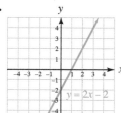

2.
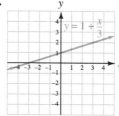

3.
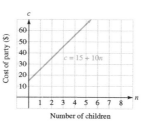

4.
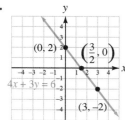

5.
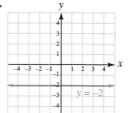

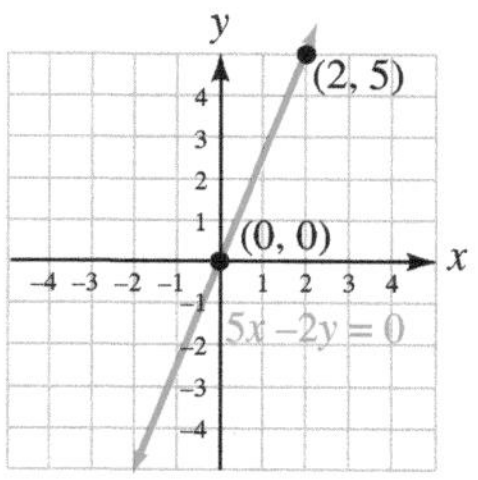

7.

8.
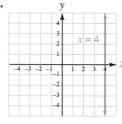

SECTION 5.4 STUDY SET

VOCABULARY

Fill in the blanks.

1. $y = 9x + 5$ is an equation in _____ variables, x and y.

2. A _____ of an equation in two variables is an ordered pair of numbers that makes the equation a true statement.

3. Solutions of equations in two variables are often listed in a _____ of solutions.

4. $y = 3x + 8$ is a _____ equation and its graph is a line.

5. The _____ form of a linear equation in two variables is $Ax + By = C$.

6. The _____ of a line is the point where the line intersects/crosses the x-axis.

7. The y-intercept of a line is the point where the line _____ the y-axis.

8. The graph of $y = 4$ is a _____ line and the graph of $x = 6$ is a _____ line.

CONCEPTS

9. Consider: $y = -3x + 6$
   a. How many variables does the equation contain?
   b. Does   satisfy the equation?
   c. Is   a solution of the equation?
   d. How many solutions does this equation have?

10. To graph a linear equation, three solutions were found, they were plotted (in black), and a straight line was drawn through them, as shown below.
   a. Looking at the graph, complete the table of solutions.
   b. From the graph, determine three other solutions of the equation.

x	y	(x, y)
-4		(,)
-1		(,)
1		(,)

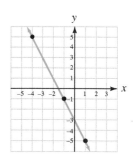

11. Find the exponent on each variable.
    a. $y = 2x - 6$
    b. $y = x^2 - 6$
    c. $y = x^3 + 2$

12. In a linear equation in x and y, what are the exponents on x and y?

13. Fill in the blanks.
    a. To find the y-intercept of the graph of a line, substitute ▢ for x in the equation and solve for ▢.
    b. To find the x-intercept of the graph of a line, substitute ▢ for y in the equation and solve for ▢.

14. Complete the table of solutions and fill in the blanks.

$$3x + 2y = 6$$

x	y	(x, y)	
0	▢	▢	← ▢-intercept
▢	0	▢	← ▢-intercept
−2	▢	▢	← ▢ point

15. Suppose you are making a table of solutions for each given equation. What three x-values would you select to make the calculations for finding the corresponding y-values the easiest?
    a. $y = \frac{4}{5}x + 2$ b. $y = 0.6x + 500$

16. Consider the graph of a linear equation shown below.
    a. Why will the coordinates of point A yield a true statement when substituted into the equation?
    b. Why will the coordinates of point B yield a false statement when substituted into the equation?

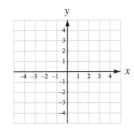

17. A student found three solutions of a linear equation and plotted them as shown. What conclusion can he make?

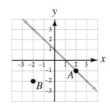

18. How many solutions are there for a linear equation in two variables?

19. $5x - y = 3$

x	y
0	
	0
1	

20. On the coordinate system below, draw the graph of a line.
    a. with no x-intercept.
    b. with no y-intercept.
    c. with an x-intercept of $(2, 0)$.
    d. with a y-intercept of $\left(0, -\frac{5}{2}\right)$.

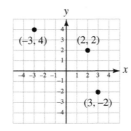

21. What is the equation of the x-axis? What is the equation of the y-axis?

22. Write the coordinates that are improper fractions as mixed numbers.
    a. $\left(\frac{7}{2}, 0\right)$ b. $\left(0, -\frac{17}{3}\right)$

23. A table of solutions for a linear equation is shown below. When constructing the graph of the equation, how would you scale the x-axis and the y-axis?

x	y	(x, y)
−20	600	$(-20, 600)$
5	100	$(5, 100)$
35	−500	$(35, -500)$

24. Complete the labeling of the table of solutions and the axis of the graph of $c = -a + 4$.

▢	▢	(▢)
−1	5	$(-1, 5)$
0	4	$(0, 4)$
2	2	$(2, 2)$

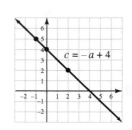

GUIDED PRACTICE

Classify each of the following as the graph of a linear equation or of a nonlinear equation. **See Objective 1.**

25. a. 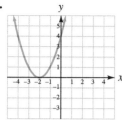 **b.**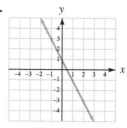

26. a. 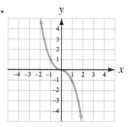 **b.**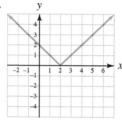

Classify each equation as linear or nonlinear. **See Objective 1.**

27. a. $y = x^3$ **b.** $2x + 3y = 6$

28. a. $y = -2$ **b.** $y = |x + 2|$

Find three solutions of the equation and draw its graph. **See Example 1.**

29. $y = 2x + 1$ **30.** $y = 3x - 2$

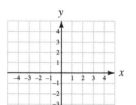   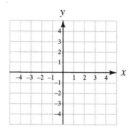

31. $y = -x + 2$ **32.** $y = -x - 1$

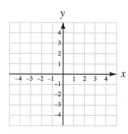   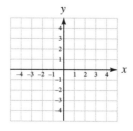

33. $y = x$ **34.** $y = 3x$

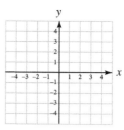   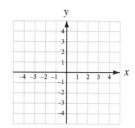

35. $y = -3x$ **36.** $y = -2x$

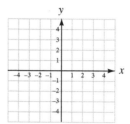   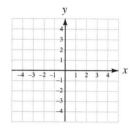

Solve each equation for y, find three solutions of the equation, and then draw its graph. **See Example 2.**

37. $2y = 4x - 6$ **38.** $3y = 6x - 3$

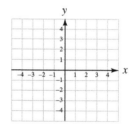   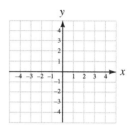

39. $2y = x - 4$ **40.** $4y = x + 16$

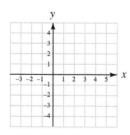   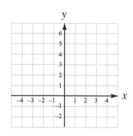

Give the coordinates of the intercepts of each graph. **See Objective 4.**

41. 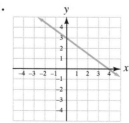   **42.**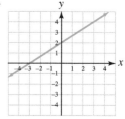

43.

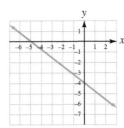

44.

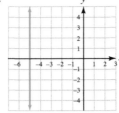

45.

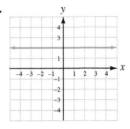

46.

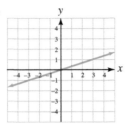

Estimate the coordinates of the intercepts of each graph. (Some are not integers.). (Answers may vary.)

47.

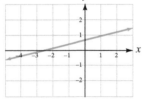

48.

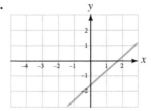

Graph each equation using the intercept method. See Example 4.

49. $2y - 2x = 6$

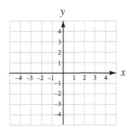

50. $3x - 3y = 9$

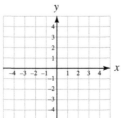

51. $4x + 5y = 20$

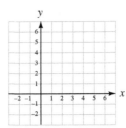

52. $3x + y = -3$

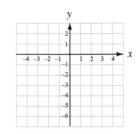

Use the intercept method to graph each equation. See Examples 5.

53. $3x + 5y = 0$

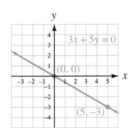

54. $4x + 3y = 0$

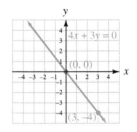

55. $2x - 7y = 0$

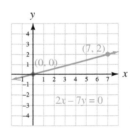

56. $6x - 5y = 0$

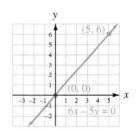

Graph each equation. See Examples 7 and 8.

57. $y = 4$

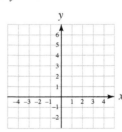

58. $y = -3$

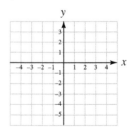

59. $x = -2$

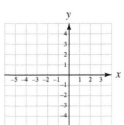

60. $x = 5$

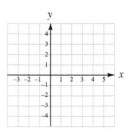

TRY IT YOURSELF

Graph each equation.

61. $15y + 5x = -15$

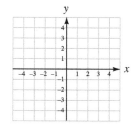

62. $8x + 4y = -24$

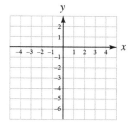

63. $3x + 4y = 8$

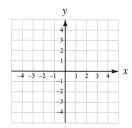

64. $2x + 3y = 9$

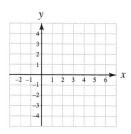

65. $y = \dfrac{x}{3}$

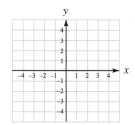

66. $y = -\dfrac{x}{3} - 1$

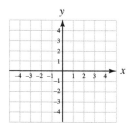

67. $-4y + 9x = -9$

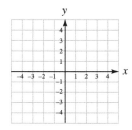

68. $-4y + 5x = -15$

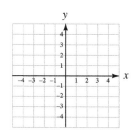

69. $3x + 4y = 12$

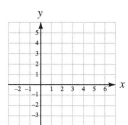

70. $4x - 3y = 12$

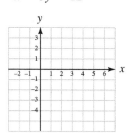

71. $y = -\dfrac{1}{2}$

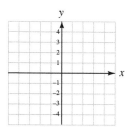

72. $y = \dfrac{5}{2}$

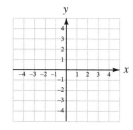

73. $x = \dfrac{4}{3}$

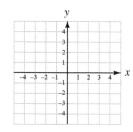

74. $x = -\dfrac{5}{3}$

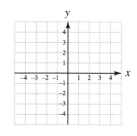

75. $y = -\dfrac{3}{2}x + 2$

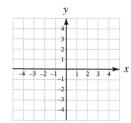

76. $y = \dfrac{2}{3}x - 2$

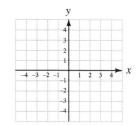

77. $2y + x = -2$

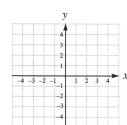

78. $4y + 2x = -8$

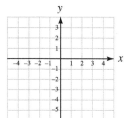

CONCEPT EXTENSIONS

Complete each table of solutions.

79. $5y = 2x + 10$

x	y
10	
	0
5	

80. $2x + 4y = 24$

x	y
4	
	7
-4	

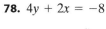

81. Match each graph with its equation.

a. $x = 2$ b. $y = 2$ c. $y = 2x$
d. $2x - y = 2$ e. $y = 2x + 2$ f. $y = -2x$

i.
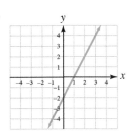

ii.
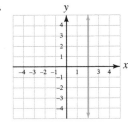

iii.
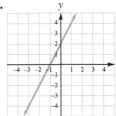

iv.
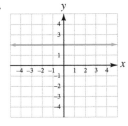

v.
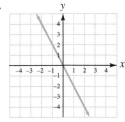

vi.
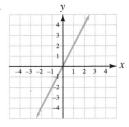

82. Fill in the blanks so that the graph of the equation below has y-intercept $(0, 3)$ and x-intercept $\left(-\dfrac{9}{4}, 0\right)$.

   ▢ $y -$ ▢ $x = 9$

APPLICATIONS

83. EDUCATION COSTS Each semester, a college charges a services fee of $50 plus $25 for each unit taken by a student.

a. Write a linear equation that gives the total enrollment cost c for a student taking u units.

b. Complete the table of solutions in the next column and graph the equation.

c. Use the graph to find the total cost for a student taking 18 units the first semester and 12 units the second semester.

d. What does the y-intercept of the line tell you?

u	c
4	
8	
14	

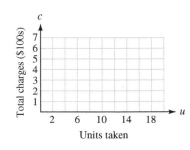

84. GROUP RATES To promote the sale of tickets for a cruise to Alaska, a travel agency reduces the regular ticket price of $3,000 by $5 for each individual traveling in the group.

a. Write a linear equation that would find the ticket price t for the cruise if a group of p people travel together.

b. Complete the table of solutions on the next page and graph the equation.

c. As the size of the group increases, what happens to the ticket price?

d. Use the graph to determine the cost of an individual ticket if a group of 25 will be traveling together.

p	t
10	
30	
60	

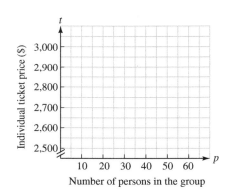

85. PHYSIOLOGY Physiologists have found that a woman's height h (in inches) can be approximated using the linear equation $h = 3.9r + 28.9$, where r represents the length of her radius bone in inches.

a. Complete the table of solutions on the next page. Round to the nearest tenth and then graph the equation.

b. Complete this sentence: From the graph, we see that the longer the radius bone, the ...

c. From the graph, estimate the height of a woman whose radius bone is 7.5 inches long.

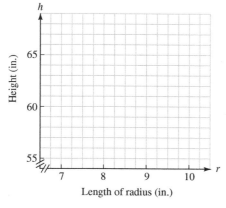

r	h
7	
8.5	
9	

86. RESEARCH EXPERIMENTS A psychology major found that the time t (in seconds) that it took a white rat to complete a maze was related to the number of trials n the rat had been given. The resulting equation was $t = 25 - 0.25n$.

a. Complete the table of solutions and graph the equation.

b. Complete this sentence: From the graph, we see that the more trials the rat had, the …

c. From the graph, estimate the time it will take the rat to complete the maze on its 32nd trial.

d. What information about the experiment does the t-intercept give?

n	t
4	
12	
16	

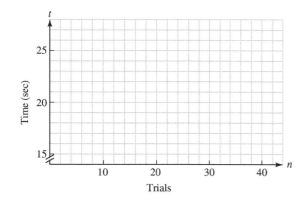

87. U.S. AUTOMOBILE ACCIDENTS The number n of lives saved by seat belts during the years 2000–2009 is estimated by $n = 170t + 13{,}800$, where t is the number of years after 2000. Graph this equation and use the graph to predict the number of lives that will be saved by seat belts in 2015. (Source: NHTSA National Center for Statistics.)

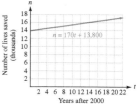

88. RAFFLES A private school is going to sell raffle tickets as a fund raiser. Suppose the number n of raffle tickets that will be sold is predicted by the equation $n = -20p + 300$, where p is the price of a raffle ticket in dollars. Graph the equation and use the graph to predict the number of raffle tickets that will be sold at a price of $6.

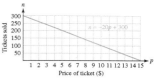

89. GAS MILEAGE The mileage for a Honda Insight traveling between 55 mph and 75 mph is estimated by the equation $m = -\frac{3}{4}s + 95$, where s is the speed of the car (in mph) and m is the mileage (in miles per gallon). Graph the equation for s between 55 and 75. Estimate the speed at which the mileage of the car drops below 40 miles per gallon. (Source: *Consumer Reports* 9/10/2009)

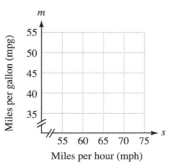

90. a. Refer to the graph. Which intercept tells the purchase price of the machinery? What was that price?

b. Which intercept indicates when the machinery will have lost all of its value? When is that?

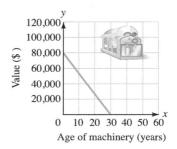

91. CHEMISTRY The relationship between the temperature T and volume V of a gas kept in a sealed container at a constant pressure is graphed below. The T-intercept of this graph is a very important scientific fact. It represents the lowest possible temperature, called **absolute zero**.

a. Estimate absolute zero.

b. What is the volume of the gas when the temperature is absolute zero?

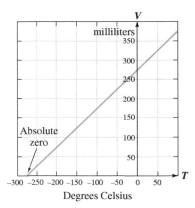

92. PHYSICS The graph shows the length L of a stretched spring (in inches) as different weights w (in pounds) are attached to it. What information about the spring does the L-intercept give?

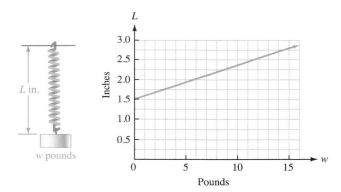

93. BOTTLED WATER DISPENSER The graph in the next column shows the number of gallons g of water remaining in a bottle after c six-ounce cups have been served from it. Find the intercepts of the graph. What information do they give?

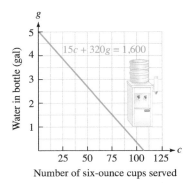

Number of six-ounce cups served

94. EGGS The number of eggs eaten by an average American in one year has remained almost constant since the year 2000. See the graph below. Draw a horizontal line that passes through, or near, the data points. What is the equation of the line?

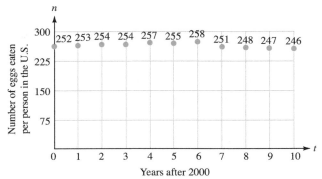

Source: United Egg

95. A linear equation and a graph are two ways of mathematically describing a relationship between two quantities. Which do you think is more informative and why?

96. From geometry, we know that two points determine a line. Explain why it is a good practice when graphing linear equations to find and plot three points instead of just two.

97. How can we tell by looking at an equation whether its graph will be a straight line?

98. Can the x-intercept and the y-intercept of a line be the same point? Explain.

99. To graph $3x + 2y = 12$, a student found the intercepts and a check point, and graphed them, as shown in figure (a). Instead of drawing a crooked line through the points, what should he have done?

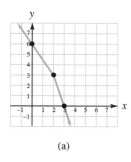

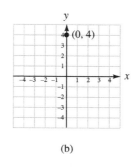

(a)   (b)

100. A student graphed the linear equation $y = 4$, as shown above in figure (b). Explain her error.

101. How do we find the intercepts of the graph of an equation without having to graph the equation?

102. Both graphs below are of the same linear equation $y = 10x$. Why do the graphs have a different appearance?

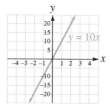

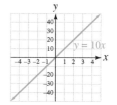

103. In Section 5.3, we discussed a method to graph $y = -2x - 2$. In Section 5.4, we discussed a method to graph $3x - 2y = 8$. Briefly explain the steps involved in each method.

104. What is the least number of intercepts a line can have? What is the greatest number a line can have? Give examples.

<hr>

SECTION 5.5

Applications Introduction Rate of Change and Slope of a Line

Our world is one of constant change. One way to mathematically represent change is using a **ratio** or a **rate.**

Ratios and Rates

A **ratio** is a comparison of two numbers using a quotient. In symbols, if a and b are two numbers, the ratio of a to b is $\dfrac{a}{b}$. Ratios that are used to compare quantities with different units are called **rates.**

Here are some examples of rates, expressed first in fractional form, and then in simplified form:

- During the first three months of 2012, *Facebook* added about 36,000,000 new users worldwide over a 90-day period. That's a growth rate of

  $\dfrac{36,000,000 \, \text{new users}}{90 \, \text{days}}$, or 400,000 new users per day.

- In 2012, the median value and median size of a North Carolina home was $130,000 and 1,625 square feet, respectively. That's $\dfrac{\$130,000}{1,625 \, \text{ft}^2}$, or $80 per square foot.

- The fastest elevator in the Empire State Building in New York moves at a rate of 1,400 feet per minute. That's $\dfrac{1,400 \, \text{feet}}{60 \, \text{seconds}}$, or 23.3 feet per second.

1. NEWSPAPERS The line graphs below model the approximate number of morning and evening newspapers published in the United States for the years 1990–2008. In this problem, you will find what is called the **average rate of increase** in the number of morning newspapers published in the U.S. and the **average rate of decrease** in the number of evening newspapers published in the U.S. over that time span.

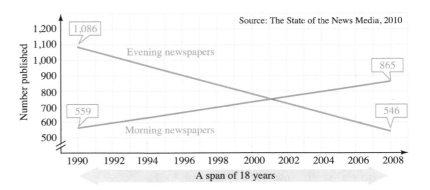

a. Use subtraction to find the change in the number of morning newspapers published in 2008 compared to 1990.

b. The growth in the number of morning newspapers shown in the graph is over how many years?

c. Fill in the blanks.

$$\text{Average rate of change} = \frac{\text{change in number of morning newspapers}}{\text{change in time}}$$ A rate of change is a ratio that includes units.

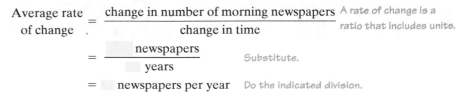

$$= \frac{\boxed{} \text{ newspapers}}{\boxed{} \text{ years}}$$ Substitute.

$$= \boxed{} \text{ newspapers per year}$$ Do the indicated division.

Thus, the number of morning newspapers published in the U.S. increased, on average, at a rate of ▢ per year from 1990 through 2008.

d. Use subtraction to find the change in the number of evening newspapers published in 2008 compared to 1990. (Hint: your answer should be negative.)

e. The decline in the number of evening newspapers shown in the graph is over how many years?

f. Fill in the blanks:

$$\text{Average rate of change} = \frac{\text{change in number of evening newspapers}}{\text{change in time}}$$

$$= \frac{\boxed{} \text{ newspapers}}{\boxed{} \text{ years}}$$ Substitute.

$$= \boxed{} \text{ newspapers per year}$$ Do the indicated division.

Thus, the number of evening newspapers published in the U.S. decreased, on average, at a rate of ▢ per year from 1990 through 2008.

In the newspaper example, we measured the steepness of the lines in the graph to determine the average rates of change. In doing so, we found the *slope* of each line. The **slope of a line** is a ratio that compares the vertical change to the corresponding horizontal change as we move along the line from one point to another.

To determine the slope of a line (usually denoted by the letter *m*) from its graph, we first pick two points on the line. Then we write the ratio of the vertical change,

called the **rise**, to the corresponding horizontal change, called the **run**, as we move
from one point to the other.

$$m = \frac{\text{vertical change}}{\text{horizontal change}} = \frac{\text{rise}}{\text{run}}$$

2.   SIDEWALKS A 16-inch-long level and a ruler are used to find the slope of the
sidewalk shown in the illustration. Determine the rise from the markings on the
ruler. Use that information to fill in the blanks.

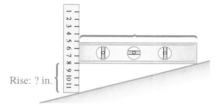

Rise: ? in.

$$m = \frac{\text{rise}}{\text{run}} = \frac{\blacksquare}{\blacksquare}$$

Now simplify the fraction:

$$m = \frac{\blacksquare}{\blacksquare}$$

3.   LADDERS Determine the rise and run from the illustration. Then fill in the
blanks to find the slope of the ladder.

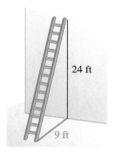

24 ft

9 ft

$$m = \frac{\text{rise}}{\text{run}} = \frac{\blacksquare}{\blacksquare}$$

Now simplify the fraction. Leave you answer as improper fraction.

$$m = \frac{\blacksquare}{\blacksquare}$$

4.   RAMPS Determine the rise and run from the illustration. Then fill in the
blanks to find the slope of the handicap ramp.

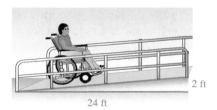

2 ft

24 ft

$$m = \frac{\text{rise}}{\text{run}} = \frac{\blacksquare}{\blacksquare}$$

Now simplify the fraction.

$$m = \frac{\blacksquare}{\blacksquare}$$

5. ROOFS Determine the rise and run from the carpenter's square in the illustration. Then fill in the blanks to find the slope of the roof.

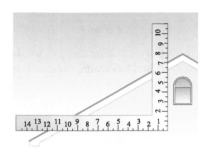

$$m = \frac{\text{rise}}{\text{run}} = \frac{\quad}{\quad}$$

6. FLYING A jet descends in a stairstep pattern, as shown in the illustration. (The symbol ′ stands for feet.) The required elevations of the plane's path are given.

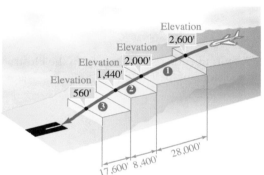

Based on data from *Los Angeles Times* (August 7, 1997), p. A8

a. To find the slope of the descent during stage 1 of the landing pattern, find the change in elevation (vertical change) using subtraction. You should get a negative answer. Then determine the horizontal change for stage 1 from the illustration. Use that information to fill in the blanks.

$$m = \frac{\text{vertical change}}{\text{horizontal change}} = \frac{\quad}{\quad}$$

Now simplify the fraction:

$$m = -\frac{\quad}{\quad}$$

b. To find the slope of the descent during stage 2 of the landing pattern, find the change in elevation (vertical change) using subtraction. You should get a negative answer. Then determine the horizontal change for stage 2 from the illustration. Use that information to fill in the blanks.

$$m = \frac{\text{vertical change}}{\text{horizontal change}} = \frac{\quad}{\quad}$$

Now simplify the fraction:

$$m = -\frac{\quad}{\quad}$$

c. To find the slope of the descent during stage 3 of the landing pattern, find the change in elevation (vertical change) using subtraction. You should get a negative answer. Then determine the horizontal change for stage 3 from the illustration. Use that information to fill in the blanks.

$$m = \frac{\text{vertical change}}{\text{horizontal change}} = \frac{\rule{1cm}{0.4pt}}{\rule{1cm}{0.4pt}}$$

Now simplify the fraction:

$$m = -\frac{\rule{0.6cm}{0.4pt}}{\rule{0.6cm}{0.4pt}}$$

d. Which stage of the landing pattern, 1, 2, or 3, is the steepest?

SECTION **5.5**
Slope and Rate of Change

Objectives

1. Find rates of change.
2. Find the slope of a line from its graph.
3. Find the slope of a line given two points.
4. Recognize positive and negative slope.
5. Find slopes of horizontal and vertical lines.
6. Solve applications of slope.
7. Use slope to graph a line.
8. Determine whether lines are parallel or perpendicular using slope.

ARE YOU READY?

The following problems review some basic skills that are needed to find the slope of a line.

1. Evaluate: $\dfrac{4 - 1}{8 - 3}$

2. Evaluate: $\dfrac{-10 - 1}{-4 - (-4)}$

3. Multiply: $-\dfrac{7}{9} \cdot \dfrac{9}{7}$

4. Simplify: $\dfrac{15}{18}$

Since our world is one of constant change, we must be able to describe change so that we can plan for the future. In this section, we will show how to describe the amount of change of one quantity in relation to the amount of change of another quantity by finding a **rate of change.**

1   Find rates of change.

The line graph in figure (a) below shows the number of business permits issued each month by a city over a 12-month period. From the shape of the graph, we can see that the number of permits issued *increased* each month.

For situations such as the one graphed in (a), it is often useful to calculate a rate of increase (called a **rate of change**). We do so by finding the **ratio** of the change in the number of business permits issued each month to the number of months over which that change took place.

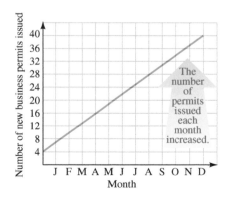

(a)

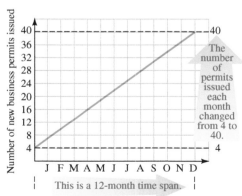

(b)

> ### Ratios and Rates
>
> A **ratio** is the quotient of two numbers or the quotient of two quantities with the same units. In symbols, if a and b represent two numbers, the ratio of a to b is $\frac{a}{b}$. Ratios that are used to compare quantities with different units are called **rates.**

In figure (b), we see that the number of permits issued prior to the month of January was 4. By the end of the year, the number of permits issued during the month of December was 40. This is a change of $40 - 4$, or 36, over a 12-month period. So we have

$$\text{Rate of change} = \frac{\text{change in number of permits issued each month}}{\text{change in time}}$$

The rate of change is a ratio.

$$= \frac{36 \text{ permits}}{12 \text{ months}}$$

$$= \frac{\overset{1}{\cancel{12}} \cdot 3 \text{ permits}}{\underset{1}{\cancel{12}} \text{ months}}$$

Factor 36 as 12 · 3 and remove the common factor of 12.

$$= \frac{3 \text{ permits}}{1 \text{ month}}$$

The number of business permits being issued increased at a rate of 3 per month, denoted as 3 permits/month.

> ***The Language of Algebra***   The preposition *per* means for each, or for every. When we say the rate of change is 3 permits *per* month, we mean 3 permits for each month.

Self Check 1

Find the rate of change in the number of subscribers over the second 5-year period. Write the rate in simplest form.

Now Try **Problem 20**

EXAMPLE 1   The graph shows the number of subscribers to a newspaper. Find the rate of change in the number of subscribers over the first 5-year period. Write the rate in simplest form.

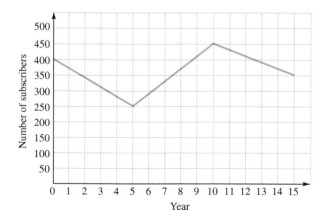

Strategy We will form a ratio of the change in the number of subscribers over the change in the time.

WHY The rate of change is given by this ratio.

Solution

$$\text{Rate of change} = \frac{\text{change in number of subscribers}}{\text{change in time}}$$ Set up the ratio.

$$= \frac{(250 - 400) \text{ subscribers}}{(5 - 0) \text{ years}}$$ Subtract the later number of subscribers from the earlier number of subscribers.

$$= \frac{-150 \text{ subscribers}}{5 \text{ years}}$$ $250 - 400 = -150$

$$= \frac{-30 \cdot \overset{1}{5} \text{ subscribers}}{\underset{1}{5} \text{ years}}$$ Factor -150 as $-30 \cdot 5$ and divide out the common factor of 5.

$$= \frac{-30 \text{ subscribers}}{1 \text{ year}}$$

The number of subscribers for the first 5 years *decreased* by 30 per year, as indicated by the negative sign in the result. We can write this as -30 subscribers/year.

2 Find the slope of a line from its graph.

The **slope of a nonvertical line** is a number that measures the line's steepness. We can calculate the slope by picking two points on the line and writing the ratio of the vertical change (called the **rise**) to the corresponding horizontal change (called the **run**) as we move from one point to the other. As an example, we will find the slope of the line that was used to describe the number of building permits issued and show that it gives the rate of change.

In the following figure, the line passes through points $P(0, 4)$ and $Q(12, 40)$. Moving along the line from point P to point Q causes the value of y to change from $y = 4$ to $y = 40$, an increase of $40 - 4 = 36$ units. We say that the *rise* is 36.

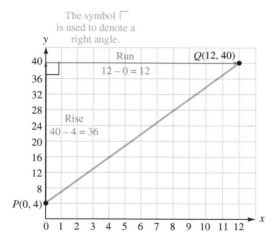

Moving from point P to point Q, the value of x increases from $x = 0$ to $x = 12$, an increase of $12 - 0 = 12$ units. We say that the *run* is 12. The slope of a line, usually denoted with the letter m, is defined to be the ratio of the change in y to the change in x.

$$m = \frac{\text{change in } y\text{-values}}{\text{change in } x\text{-values}}$$ Slope is a ratio.

$$= \frac{40 - 4}{12 - 0}$$ To find the change in y (the rise), subtract the y-values. To find the change in x (the run), subtract the x-values.

$$= \frac{36}{12} \qquad \text{Perform the subtractions.}$$

$$= 3 \qquad \text{Perform the division.}$$

This is the same value we obtained when we found the rate of change of the number of business permits issued over the 12-month period. Therefore, by finding the slope of the line, we found a rate of change.

Self Check 2

Find the slope of the line using two points different from those used in Example 2.

Now Try **Problem 27**

EXAMPLE 2   Find the slope of the line shown in figure (a).

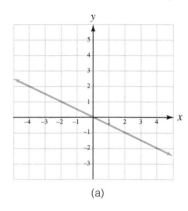

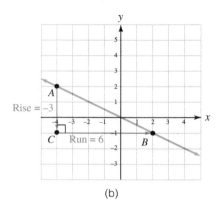

(a)   (b)

Strategy We will pick two points on the line, construct a slope triangle, and find the rise and the run. Then we will write the ratio of the rise to the run.

WHY The slope of a line is the ratio of the rise to the run.

Solution

We begin by choosing two points on the line—call them A and B—as shown in figure (b). One way to move from point A to point B is to start at point A and count *downward* 3 grid squares. Because this movement is downward, the rise is -3. Then, moving right, we count 6 grid squares to reach B. This indicates a run of 6. These steps create a right triangle called a **slope triangle.** To find the slope of the line, we write a ratio of rise to run in simplified form. Usually the letter m is used to denote slope, so we have

$$m = \frac{\text{rise}}{\text{run}} \qquad \text{The slope of a line is the ratio of the rise to the run.}$$

$$m = \frac{-3}{6} \qquad \text{From the slope triangle, the rise is } -3 \text{ and the run is 6.}$$

$$m = -\frac{1}{2} \qquad \text{Simplify the fraction.}$$

The slope of the line is $-\frac{1}{2}$.

Success Tip   The answers from Example 2 and the Self Check illustrate an important fact about slope: *The same value for the slope of a line will result no matter which two points on the line are used to determine the rise and the run.*

3 **Find the slope of a line given two points.**

We can generalize the graphic method for finding slope to develop a slope formula. To begin, we select points P and Q on the line shown in the figure on the next page. To distinguish between the coordinates of these points, we use **subscript notation.** Point P has coordinates (x_1, y_1), which are read as "x sub 1 and y sub 1." Point Q has coordinates (x_2, y_2), which are read as "x sub 2 and y sub 2."

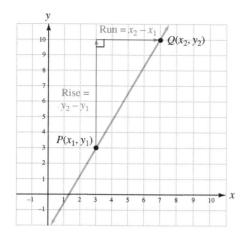

As we move from P to Q, the rise is the difference of the y-coordinates: $y_2 - y_1$. We call this difference the **change in y.** The run is the difference of the x-coordinates: $x_2 - x_1$. This difference is called the **change in x.** Since the slope is the ratio $\frac{\text{rise}}{\text{run}}$, we have the following formula for calculating slope.

Slope of a Nonvertical Line

The **slope** of a nonvertical line passing through points (x_1, y_1) and (x_2, y_2) is

$$m = \frac{\text{vertical change}}{\text{horizontal change}} = \frac{\text{rise}}{\text{run}} = \frac{\text{change in } y}{\text{change in } x} = \frac{y_2 - y_1}{x_2 - x_1} \quad \text{if } x_2 \neq x_1$$

EXAMPLE 3   Find the slope of the line passing through $(1, 2)$ and $(3, 8)$.

Strategy We will use the slope formula to find the slope of the line.

WHY We know the coordinates of two points on the line.

Solution
When using the slope formula, it makes no difference which point you call (x_1, y_1) and which point you call (x_2, y_2). If we let (x_1, y_1) be $(1, 2)$ and (x_2, y_2) be $(3, 8)$, then

$m = \dfrac{y_2 - y_1}{x_2 - x_1}$ This is the slope formula.

$m = \dfrac{8 - 2}{3 - 1}$ Substitute 8 for y_2, 2 for y_1, 3 for x_2, and 1 for x_1.

$m = \dfrac{6}{2}$ Do the subtractions.

$m = 3$ Simplify. Think of this as a $\frac{3}{1}$ rise-to-run ratio.

The slope of the line is 3. The graph of the line, including the slope triangle, is shown here. Note that we obtain the same value for the slope if we let $(x_1, y_1) = (3, 8)$ and $(x_2, y_2) = (1, 2)$.

$$m = \frac{y_2 - y_1}{x_2 - x_1} = \frac{2 - 8}{1 - 3} = \frac{-6}{-2} = 3$$

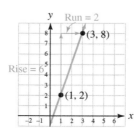

Self Check 3

Find the slope of the line passing through $(2, 1)$ and $(4, 11)$.

Now Try **Problem 33**

Caution!   When finding the slope of a line, always subtract the *y*-values and the *x*-values in the same order. Otherwise your answer will have the wrong sign:

$$m \neq \frac{y_2 - y_1}{x_1 - x_2} \quad \text{and} \quad m \neq \frac{y_1 - y_2}{x_2 - x_1}$$

THINK IT THROUGH   *Average Rate of Tuition Increase*

"Although four-year schools get all the media hype, many high school graduates head right to a two-year institution. Looking at the facts, it's no surprise why. Cheaper, quicker, and highly vocational, two-year schools offer students the chance to start their careers sooner and with less (or no) debt."

CollegeView

The line graphed below approximates the average cost of tuition and fees at U.S. public two-year academic institutions for the years 1990–2011. Find the average rate of increase in cost over this time period by finding the slope of the line.

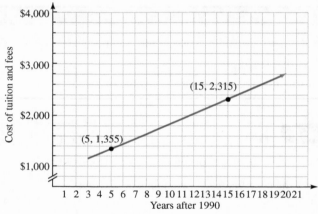

Source: The College Board

Self Check 4

Find the slope of the line that passes through $(-1, -2)$ and $(1, -7)$.

Now Try **Problem 39**

EXAMPLE 4   Find the slope of the line that passes through $(-2, 4)$ and $(5, -6)$ and draw its graph.

Strategy We will use the slope formula to find the slope of the line.

WHY We know the coordinates of two points on the line.

Solution

Since we know the coordinates of two points on the line, we can find its slope. If (x_1, y_1) is $(-2, 4)$ and (x_2, y_2) is $(5, -6)$, then

$$\begin{aligned} x_1 &= -2 \\ y_1 &= 4 \end{aligned} \quad \text{and} \quad \begin{aligned} x_2 &= 5 \\ y_2 &= -6 \end{aligned}$$

$$m = \frac{y_2 - y_1}{x_2 - x_1} \qquad \text{{\footnotesize This is the slope formula.}}$$

$$m = \frac{-6 - 4}{5 - (-2)} \qquad \text{{\footnotesize Substitute −6 for } } y_2 \text{, 4 for } y_1 \text{, 5 for } x_2 \text{, and −2 for } x_1.$$

$$m = -\frac{10}{7} \qquad \text{{\footnotesize Simplify the numerator: −6 − 4 = −10.}}\\ \text{{\footnotesize Simplify the denominator: 5 − (−2) = 7.}}$$

The slope of the line is $-\frac{10}{7}$. The figure below shows the graph of the line. Note that the line falls from left to right—a fact that is indicated by its negative slope.

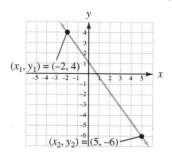

4   Recognize positive and negative slope.

In Example 3, the slope of the line was positive (3). In Example 4, the slope of the line was negative $\left(-\frac{10}{7}\right)$. In general, lines that rise from left to right have a positive slope, and lines that fall from left to right have a negative slope, as shown below.

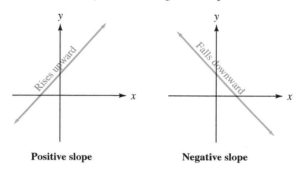

Positive slope   **Negative slope**

5   Find slopes of horizontal and vertical lines.

In the next two examples, we will calculate the slope of a horizontal line and show that a vertical line has no defined slope.

EXAMPLE 5   Find the slope of the line $y = 3$.

Strategy We will find the coordinates of two points on the line.

WHY We can then use the slope formula to find the slope of the line.

Solution
To find the slope of the line $y = 3$, we need to know two points on the line. Graph the horizontal line $y = 3$ and label two points on the line: $(-2, 3)$ and $(3, 3)$.
    If (x_1, y_1) is $(-2, 3)$ and (x_2, y_2) is $(3, 3)$, we have

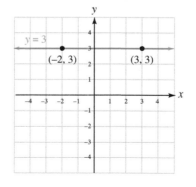

$$m = \frac{y_2 - y_1}{x_2 - x_1} \qquad \text{This is the slope formula.}$$

$$m = \frac{3 - 3}{3 - (-2)} \qquad \begin{array}{l}\text{Substitute 3 for } y_2, \text{ 3 for}\\ y_1, \text{ 3 for } x_2, \text{ and } -2 \text{ for } x_1.\end{array}$$

$$m = \frac{0}{5} \qquad \begin{array}{l}\text{Simplify the numerator and}\\ \text{the denominator.}\end{array}$$

$$m = 0$$

The slope of the line $y = 3$ is 0.

Self Check 5
Find the slope of the line $y = -2$.

Now Try **Problem 45**

The *y*-coordinates of any two points on any horizontal line will be the same, and the *x*-values will be different. Thus, the numerator of $\frac{y_2 - y_1}{x_2 - x_1}$ will always be zero, and the denominator will always be nonzero. Therefore, the slope of a horizontal line is zero.

Self Check 6

Find the slope of $x = 5$.

Now Try **Problem 47**

EXAMPLE 6   Find the slope of the line $x = -2$.

Strategy We will find the coordinates of two points on the line.

WHY We can then use the slope formula to find the slope of the line, if it exists.

Solution

To find the slope of the line $x = -2$, we need to know two points on the line. We graph the vertical line $x = -2$ and label two points on the line: $(-2, -1)$ and $(-2, 3)$.

If (x_1, y_1) is $(-2, -1)$ and (x_2, y_2) is $(-2, 3)$, we have

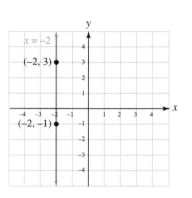

$$m = \frac{y_2 - y_1}{x_2 - x_1} \qquad \text{This is the slope formula.}$$

$$m = \frac{3 - (-1)}{-2 - (-2)} \qquad \begin{array}{l}\text{Substitute 3 for } y_2, -1 \\ \text{for } y_1, -2 \text{ for } x_2, \text{ and } -2 \\ \text{for } x_1.\end{array}$$

$$m = \frac{4}{0} \qquad \begin{array}{l}\text{Simplify the numerator} \\ \text{and the denominator.}\end{array}$$

Since division by zero is undefined, $\frac{4}{0}$ has no meaning. The slope of the line $x = -2$ is undefined.

The *y*-values of any two points on a vertical line will be different, and the *x*-values will be the same. Thus, the numerator of $\frac{y_2 - y_1}{x_2 - x_1}$ will always be nonzero, and the denominator will always be zero. Therefore, the slope of a vertical line is undefined.

We now summarize the results from Examples 5 and 6.

Slopes of Horizontal and Vertical Lines

Horizontal lines (lines with equations of the form $y = b$) have a slope of 0.

Vertical lines (lines with equations of the form $x = a$) have undefined slope.

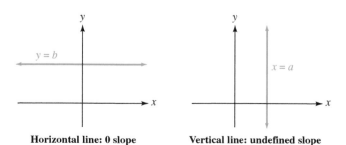

Horizontal line: 0 slope   Vertical line: undefined slope

6 Solve applications of slope.

The concept of slope has many applications. For example, architects use slope when designing ramps and roofs. Truckers must be aware of the slope, or **grade,** of the roads they travel. Mountain bikers ride up rocky trails and snow skiers speed down steep slopes.

12 ft   1 ft

100 ft   15 ft

The Americans with Disabilities Act provides a guideline for the steepness of a ramp. The maximum slope for a wheelchair ramp is 1 foot of rise for every 12 feet of run: $m = \dfrac{1}{12}$.

The grade of an incline is its slope expressed as a percent: A 15% grade means a rise of 15 feet for every run of 100 feet: $m = \dfrac{15}{100}$, which simplifies to $\dfrac{3}{20}$. A grade is always expressed as a positive percent.

> **Success Tip**   The key to applying the concept of slope to real-world problems is to look for a slope triangle first. Then determine the rise and run.

EXAMPLE 7   *Architecture*   **Pitch** is the incline of a roof written as a ratio of the vertical rise to the horizontal run. It is always expressed as a positive number. Find the pitch of the roof shown in the illustration.

Strategy We will determine the rise and the run of the roof from the illustration. Then we will write the ratio of the rise to the run.

WHY The pitch of a roof is its slope, and the slope of a line is the ratio of the rise to the run.

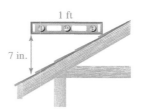

1 ft

7 in.

Solution
A level is used to create a slope triangle. The rise of the slope triangle is given as 7 inches. Since a ratio is a quotient of two quantities with the same units, we will express the length of the one-foot-long level as 12 inches. Therefore, the run of the slope triangle is 12 inches.

$$m = \frac{\text{rise}}{\text{run}} = \frac{7}{12}$$

The roof has a $\dfrac{7}{12}$ pitch. This means that the roof rises 7 units for every 12 units in the horizontal direction.

Sometimes it is helpful to use different variables in the slope formula to more closely fit the words of an application problem.

Self Check 7

ROOFING   Find the pitch of the roof.

Now Try **Problem 87**

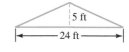

5 ft

24 ft

Self Check 8

DOWNHILL SKIING Find the
average rate of descent if the
skier completes the course in 20
minutes.

***Now Try*   Problem 95**

EXAMPLE 8   *Downhill Skiing.*   It takes a skier 25 minutes to complete
the course shown in the illustration below. Find her average rate of descent in feet
per minute.

Strategy   We will describe the skier's positions on the course as ordered pairs of the
form (time, elevation). Then we will use the slope formula to calculate the average rate
of descent.

WHY   We use the slope formula because we know the coordinates of the skier at the
beginning and at the end of the course.

Solution
The skier's position can be described as an
ordered pair of the form (time, elevation), or
more simply, (t, E). To find the average rate of
descent, we will calculate the slope of the line
passing through the points $(t_1, E_1) =
(0, 12,000)$ and $(t_2, E_2) = (25, 8,500)$ and
attach the appropriate units to the numerator
and denominator.

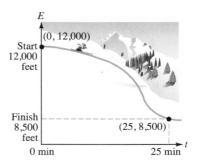

$$\text{Rate of descent} = \frac{(E_2 - E_1)\text{ feet}}{(t_2 - t_1)\text{ minutes}}$$

This is the slope formula adapted to a
coordinate system with ordered pairs of the
form (t, E).

$$= \frac{(8,500 - 12,000)\text{ feet}}{(25 - 0)\text{ minutes}}$$

Substitute 8,500 for E_2, 12,000 for E_1, 25 for
t_2, and 0 for t_1.

$$= \frac{-3,500\text{ feet}}{25\text{ minutes}}$$

Do the subtractions. The negative number
indicates a loss of elevation.

$$= -140 \text{ ft per min}$$

Do the division.

The skier's average rate of descent was 140 feet per minute. (The word *descent* itself
implies a loss of elevation during the ski run. Therefore, the negative symbol − need
not be written in front of 140.)

7 **Use slope to graph a line.**

We can graph a line whenever we know the
coordinates of one point on the line and the slope
of the line. For example, to graph the line that
passes through $P(2, 4)$ and has a slope of 3, we first
plot $P(2, 4)$, as in the figure. We can express the
slope of 3 as a fraction: $3 = \frac{3}{1}$. Therefore, the line
rises 3 units for every 1 unit it *runs* to the right. We
can find a second point on the line by starting at
$P(2, 4)$ and moving 3 units up (rise) and 1 unit to the
right (run). This brings us to a point that we will call
Q with coordinates $(2 + 1, 4 + 3)$ or $(3, 7)$. The
required line passes through points P and Q.

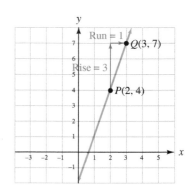

EXAMPLE 9   Graph the line that passes through the point $(-3, 4)$ with slope $-\frac{2}{5}$.

Strategy We will plot the given point and identify the rise and the run of the slope. Then we will start at the plotted point and find a second point on the line by forming a slope triangle.

WHY Once we locate two points on the line, we can draw the graph of the line.

Solution

We plot the point $(-3, 4)$ as shown in the figure to the right. Then, after writing the slope $-\frac{2}{5}$ as $\frac{-2}{5}$, we see that the *rise* is -2 and the *run* is 5. From the point $(-3, 4)$, we can find a second point on the line by moving 2 units down (rise) and then 5 units right (run). (A rise of -2 means to move down 2 units.) This brings us to the point with coordinates of $(2, 2)$. We then draw a line that passes through the two points.

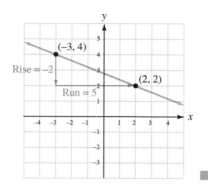

Self Check 9

Graph the line that passes through the point $(-4, 2)$ with slope -4.

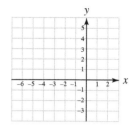

Now Try **Problem 51**

---

8 **Determine whether lines are parallel or perpendicular using slope.**

Two lines that lie in the same plane but do not intersect are called **parallel lines.** Parallel lines have the same slope and different y-intercepts. For example, the lines graphed in figure (a) are parallel because they both have slope $-\frac{2}{3}$.

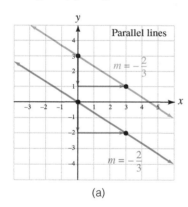

(a)

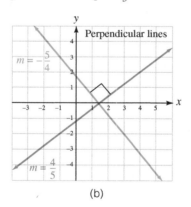

(b)

Lines that intersect to form four right angles (angles with measure 90°) are called **perpendicular lines.** If the product of the slopes of two lines is -1, the lines are perpendicular. This means that the slopes are **negative** (or **opposite**) **reciprocals.** In figure (b), we know that the lines with slopes $\frac{4}{5}$ and $-\frac{5}{4}$ are perpendicular because

$$\frac{4}{5}\left(-\frac{5}{4}\right) = -\frac{20}{20} = -1 \quad \text{\small $\frac{4}{5}$ and $-\frac{5}{4}$ are negative reciprocals.}$$

Slopes of Parallel and Perpendicular Lines

1. Two different lines with the same slope are parallel.
2. Two lines are perpendicular if the product of the slopes is -1; that is, if their slopes are negative reciprocals.
3. Any horizontal line and any vertical line are perpendicular.

Self Check 10

Determine whether the line that passes through $(2, 1)$ and $(6, 8)$ and the line that passes through $(-1, 0)$ and $(4, 7)$ are parallel, perpendicular, or neither.

Now Try **Problems 57 and 59**

EXAMPLE 10   Determine whether the line that passes through $(7, -9)$ and $(10, 2)$ and the line that passes through $(0, 1)$ and $(3, 12)$ are parallel, perpendicular, or neither.

Strategy We will use the slope formula to find the slope of each line.

WHY If the slopes are equal, the lines are parallel. If the slopes are negative reciprocals, the lines are perpendicular. Otherwise, the lines are neither parallel nor perpendicular.

Solution
To calculate the slope of each line, we use the slope formula.

The line through $(7, -9)$ and $(10, 2)$:   **The line through $(0, 1)$ and $(3, 12)$:**

$$m = \frac{y_2 - y_1}{x_2 - x_1} = \frac{2 - (-9)}{10 - 7} = \frac{11}{3} \qquad m = \frac{y_2 - y_1}{x_2 - x_1} = \frac{12 - 1}{3 - 0} = \frac{11}{3}$$

Since the slopes are the same, the lines are parallel.

Self Check 11

Find the slope of a line perpendicular to the line passing through $(-4, 1)$ and $(9, 5)$.

Now Try **Problem 67**

EXAMPLE 11   Find the slope of a line perpendicular to the line passing through $(1, -4)$ and $(8, 4)$.

Strategy We will use the slope formula to find the slope of the line passing through $(1, -4)$ and $(8, 4)$.

WHY We can then form the negative reciprocal of the result to produce the slope of a line perpendicular to the given line.

Solution
The slope of the line that passes through $(1, -4)$ and $(8, 4)$ is

$$m = \frac{y_2 - y_1}{x_2 - x_1} = \frac{4 - (-4)}{8 - 1} = \frac{8}{7}$$

The slope of a line perpendicular to the given line has slope that is the negative (or opposite) reciprocal of $\frac{8}{7}$, which is $-\frac{7}{8}$.

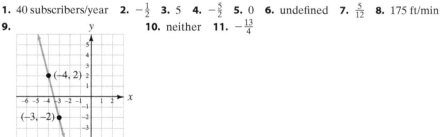

ANSWERS TO SELF CHECKS

1. 40 subscribers/year   **2.** $-\frac{1}{2}$ **3.** 5   **4.** $-\frac{5}{2}$ **5.** 0   **6.** undefined   **7.** $\frac{5}{12}$ **8.** 175 ft/min
9.   **10.** neither   **11.** $-\frac{13}{4}$

SECTION 5.5   STUDY SET

▌ VOCABULARY

Fill in the blanks.

1. A _____ is the quotient of two numbers.

2. Ratios used to compare quantities with different units are called _____.

3. The _____ of a line is defined to be the ratio of the change in y to the change in x. It is a measure of the line's steepness.

4. The vertical change between two points on a coordinate system is called the _____.

5. The horizontal change between two points on a coordinate system is called the _____.

6. $m = \dfrac{\text{\rule{1cm}{0.4pt} change}}{\text{horizontal change}} = \dfrac{\text{rise}}{\text{\rule{0.5cm}{0.4pt}}} = \dfrac{\text{change in \rule{0.5cm}{0.4pt}}}{\text{change in \rule{0.5cm}{0.4pt}}}$

7. Two lines that lie in the same plane but do not intersect are called _____ lines. _____ lines intersect to form four right angles.

8. The rate of _____ of a linear relationship can be found by finding the slope of the graph of the line and attaching the proper units.

CONCEPTS

Fill in the blanks.

9. _____ lines have a slope of 0. Vertical lines have _____ slope.

10. A line with positive slope _____ from left to right. A line with negative slope _____ from left to right.

11. In the following illustration, which line has
    a. a positive slope?
    b. a negative slope?
    c. zero slope?
    d. undefined slope?

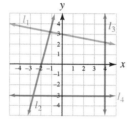

12. Consider the graph of the line in the following illustration:
    a. Find its slope using points A and B.
    b. Find its slope using points B and C.
    c. Find its slope using points A and C.
    d. What observation is suggested by your answers to parts a, b, and c?

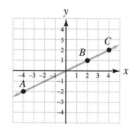

13. Consider each graph of a line and the slope triangle. What is the rise? What is the run? What is the slope of the line?

    a.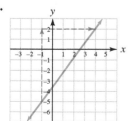
    b.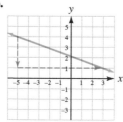

14. For each graph, determine which line has the greater slope.

    a.   b. 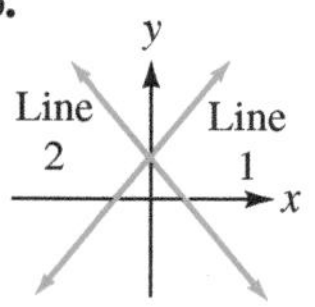   c.

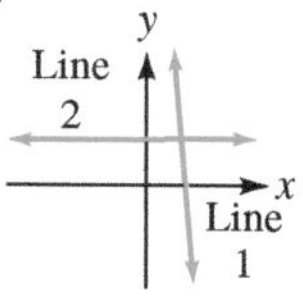

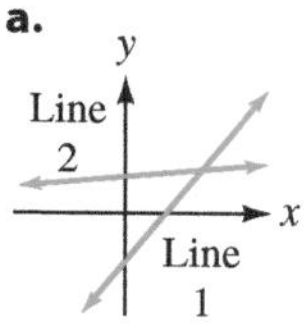

15. Which two labeled points should be used to find the slope of the line?

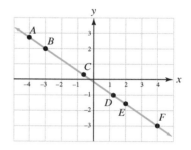

16. Evaluate each expression.

    a. $\dfrac{10 - 4}{6 - 5}$ b. $\dfrac{-1 - 1}{-2 - (-7)}$

17. Write each slope in a better way.

    a. $m = \dfrac{0}{6}$ b. $m = \dfrac{8}{0}$

    c. $m = \dfrac{3}{12}$ d. $m = \dfrac{-10}{-5}$

18. The *grade* of an incline is its slope expressed as a percent. Express the slope $\frac{2}{5}$ as a grade.

19. Fill in the blanks.
    a. Two different lines with the same slope are _____.
    b. If the slopes of two lines are negative reciprocals, the lines are _____.
    c. The product of the slopes of perpendicular lines is

20. GROWTH RATES The graph on the next page shows how a child's height increased from ages 2 through 5. Fill in the correct units to find the rate of change in the child's height.

    $$\dfrac{\text{Rate of}}{\text{change}} = \dfrac{(40 - 31)\ \rule{0.5cm}{0.4pt}}{(5 - 2)\ \rule{0.5cm}{0.4pt}}$$

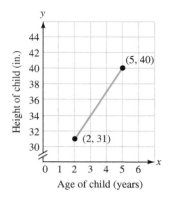

Height of child (in.)

(5, 40)

(2, 31)

Age of child (years)

NOTATION

21. Write the formula used to find the slope of the line passing through (x_1, y_1) and (x_2, y_2).

22. Explain the difference between y^2 and y_2.

23. Fill in the blanks to state the slope formula in words:

m equals y _____ two minus y _____ one

_____ x sub _____ minus x sub _____.

24. Consider the points $(7, 2)$ and $(-4, 1)$. If we let $x_1 = 7$, then what is y_2?

GUIDED PRACTICE

Find the slope of each line. See Examples 1–2.

25.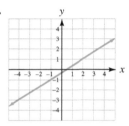

26.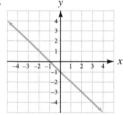

27.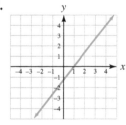

28.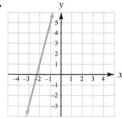

29.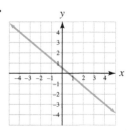

30.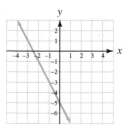

31.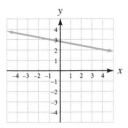

32.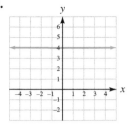

Find the slope of the line passing through the given points, when possible. See Examples 3–4.

33. $(2, 4)$ and $(1, 3)$ **34.** $(1, 3)$ and $(2, 5)$

35. $(3, 4)$ and $(2, 7)$ **36.** $(3, 6)$ and $(5, 2)$

37. $(0, 0)$ and $(4, 5)$ **38.** $(4, 3)$ and $(7, 8)$

39. $(-3, 5)$ and $(-5, 6)$ **40.** $(6, -2)$ and $(-3, 2)$

41. $(5, 7)$ and $(-4, 7)$ **42.** $(-1, -12)$ and $(6, -12)$

43. $(8, -4)$ and $(8, -3)$ **44.** $(-2, 8)$ and $(-2, 15)$

Find the slope of the graph of each line. See Examples 5–6.

45. $y = 5$ **46.** $x = -5$

47. $x = 4$ **48.** $y = -7$

Graph the line that passes through the given point and has the given slope. See Example 7.

49. $(0, 0), m = -4$ **50.** $(0, 0), m = 5$

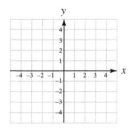

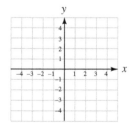

51. $(-3, -3), m = -\dfrac{3}{2}$ **52.** $(-2, -1), m = \dfrac{4}{3}$

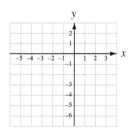

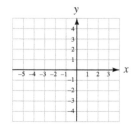

53. $(-5, 1)$, $m = 0$

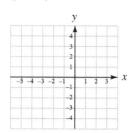

54. $(0, 3)$, undefined slope

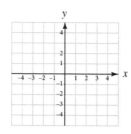

55. $(-1, -4)$, undefined slope

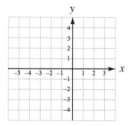

56. $(-3, -2)$, $m = 0$

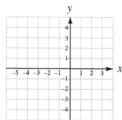

Determine whether the lines through each pair of points are parallel, perpendicular, or neither. **See Example 8.**

57. $(5, 3)$ and $(1, 4)$
   $(-3, -4)$ and $(1, -5)$

58. $(2, 4)$ and $(-1, -1)$
   $(8, 0)$ and $(11, 5)$

59. $(-4, -2)$ and $(2, -3)$
   $(7, 1)$ and $(8, 7)$

60. $(-2, 4)$ and $(6, -7)$
   $(-6, 4)$ and $(5, 12)$

61. $(2, 2)$ and $(4, -3)$
   $(-3, 4)$ and $(-1, 9)$

62. $(-1, -3)$ and $(2, 4)$
   $(5, 2)$ and $(8, -5)$

63. $(4, 2)$ and $(5, -3)$
   $(-5, 3)$ and $(-2, 9)$

64. $(8, -3)$ and $(8, -8)$
   $(11, 3)$ and $(22, 3)$

Find the slope of a line perpendicular to the line passing through the given two points. **See Example 9.**

65. $(0, 0)$ and $(5, -9)$

66. $(0, 0)$ and $(5, 12)$

67. $(-1, 7)$ and $(1, 10)$

68. $(-7, 6)$ and $(0, 4)$

CONCEPT EXTENSIONS

Find the slope of the line passing through the given points.

69. $(-2.5, 1.75)$ and $(-0.5, -7.75)$

70. $(6.4, -7.2)$ and $(-8.8, 4.2)$

71. $\left(-\frac{4}{9}, -\frac{1}{8}\right)$ and $\left(\frac{5}{9}, \frac{3}{8}\right)$

72. $\left(-\frac{3}{4}, \frac{2}{3}\right)$ and $\left(\frac{4}{3}, -\frac{1}{6}\right)$

Determine the slope of the graph of the line that has the given table of solutions. **See Examples 2 and 3.**

73.

x	y	(x, y)
-3	-1	$(-3, -1)$
1	2	$(1, 2)$

74.

x	y	(x, y)
-3	6	$(-3, 6)$
0	2	$(0, 2)$

75.

x	y	(x, y)
-3	6	$(-3, 6)$
0	6	$(0, 6)$

76.

x	y	(x, y)
4	-5	$(4, -5)$
4	0	$(4, 0)$

APPLICATIONS

77. POOL DESIGN Find the slope of the bottom of the swimming pool as it drops off from the shallow end to the deep end, as shown.

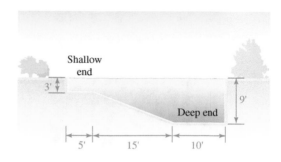

78. DRAINAGE To measure the amount of fall (slope) of a concrete patio slab, a 10-foot-long 2-by-4, a 1-foot ruler, and a level were used. Find the amount of fall in the slab. Explain what it means.

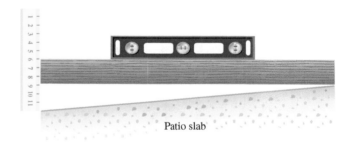

Patio slab

79. GRADE OF A ROAD The vertical fall of the road shown on the next page is 264 ft for a horizontal run of 1 mile (5,280 ft). In this question, you are to find the *grade* of the road so that a sign can be posted to warn truckers.

   a. First, find the slope of the decline. Express the result as a fraction in simplest form.

   b. Next, convert your answer in part a to a decimal.

   c. Finally, convert your answer in part b to a percent. This is the grade of the road.

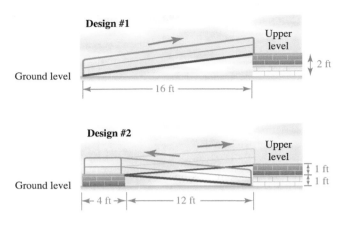

Design #1

Ground level

Upper level

2 ft

16 ft

Design #2

Ground level

Upper level

1 ft
1 ft

4 ft

12 ft

80. STREETS One of the steepest streets in the United States is Eldred Street in Highland Park, California (near Los Angeles). It rises approximately 220 feet over a horizontal distance of 665 feet. What is the grade of the street?

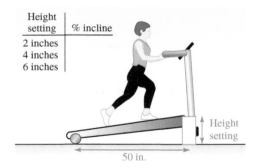

81. RAILROADS The Saluda Grade in Polk County, North Carolina, is the steepest standard-gauge mainline railway grade in the United States. At one point, the grade reaches 5.1% between the towns of Melrose and Saluda. Explain what a 5.1% grade means.

82. TREADMILLS For each height setting listed in the table, find the resulting slope of the jogging surface of the treadmill below. Express each incline as a percent.

Height setting	% incline
2 inches	
4 inches	
6 inches	

Height setting

50 in.

83. ACCESSIBILITY The illustration in the next column shows two designs to make the upper level of a stadium wheelchair-accessible.

  a. Find the slope of the ramp in design 1.

  b. Find the slopes of the ramps in design 2.

  c. Give one advantage and one drawback of each design.

84. MAPS Topographic maps have contour lines that connect points of equal elevation on a mountain. The vertical distance between contour lines in the illustration below is 50 feet. Find the slope of the west face and the slope of the east face of the mountain peak.

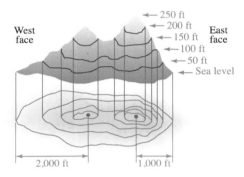

West face

East face

250 ft
200 ft
150 ft
100 ft
50 ft
Sea level

2,000 ft

1,000 ft

85. FIREFIGHTING When flames are tilted due to effects of wind, firefighters measure what is called the **slope percent** of the flames. Calculate the slope percent of the flame shown below by expressing its "slope" as a percent. (Source math.fire.org)

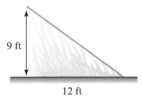

9 ft

12 ft

86. ARCHITECTURE In the diagram on the next page, locate the coordinates of the peak of the roof if it is to have a pitch of $\frac{2}{5}$ and the roof line is to pass through the two points in black.

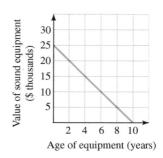

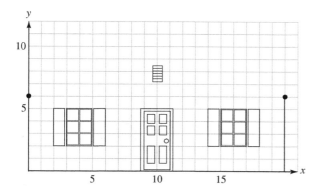

87. CARPENTRY Find the pitch of each roof.

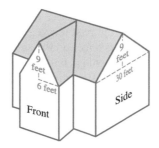

88. DOLL HOUSES Find x so that the pitch of the roof of the doll house is $\frac{4}{3}$.

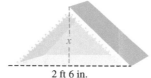

2 ft 6 in.

89. IRRIGATION The following graph shows the number of gallons of water remaining in a reservoir as water is discharged from it to irrigate a field. Find the rate of change in the number of gallons of water for the time the field was being irrigated.

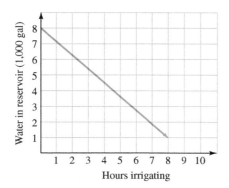

90. DEPRECIATION The graph in the next column shows how the value of some sound equipment decreased over the years. Find the rate of change of its value during this time.

91. ENGINE OUTPUT Use the graph below to find the rate of change in the horsepower (hp) produced by an automobile engine for engine speeds in the range of 2,400 − 4,800 revolutions per minute (rpm).

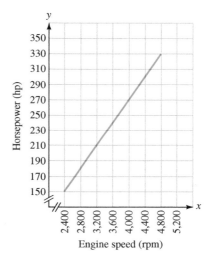

92. COMMERCIAL JETS Examine the graph and consider trips of more than 7,000 miles by a Boeing 777. Use a rate of change to estimate how the maximum payload decreases as the distance traveled increases.

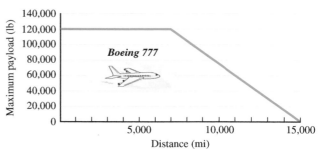

Based on data from Lawrence Livermore National Laboratory and *Los Angeles Times* (October 22, 1998).

93. MILK PRODUCTION The following graph approximates the amount of milk produced per cow in the United States for the years 1996–2009. Find the rate of change.

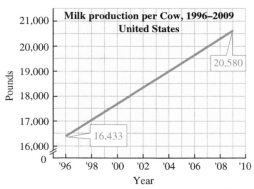

Source: USDA; Agricultural and Applied Economics, UW Madison

94. WAL-MART The following graph approximates the sales revenue of Wal-Mart for the years 1991–2009. Find the rate of change in revenue for the years.

  a. 1991–1998

  b. 1998–2009

Source: wikinvest.com

95. EXTREME SPORTS See the illustration below. Find the average rate of descent of a street luge "pilot" if he completes the course in 3 minutes.

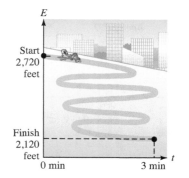

96. BIKE RACING Find the average rate of descent of a mountain biker if she completes the course in 6 minutes.

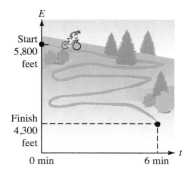

97. COMPUTERS The price of computers has been dropping for the past ten years. If a desktop PC cost $5,700 10 years ago, and the same computing power cost $400 2 years ago, find the rate of decrease per year. (Assume a straight-line model.)

98. DECKS See the illustration below. Find the slopes of the cross-brace and the supports. Is the cross-brace perpendicular to either support?

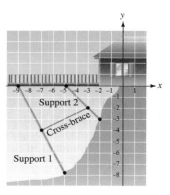

WRITING

99. Explain why the slope of a vertical line is undefined.

100. How do we distinguish between a line with positive slope and a line with negative slope?

101. Give an example of a rate of change that government officials might be interested in knowing so they can plan for the future needs of our country.

102. Explain the difference between a rate of change that is positive and one that is negative. Give an example of each.

103. SKIING The men's giant slalom course shown in the illustration is longer than the women's course. Does this mean that the men's course is steeper? Use the concept of the slope of a line to explain.

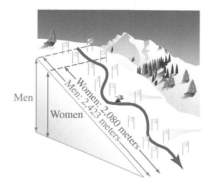

104. BOTTLED WATER Refer to the graph below. Write a paragraph that explains how the consumption of bottled water has changed. Use the words *increasing* and *decreasing*, and the phrase *rate of change* in your written answer.

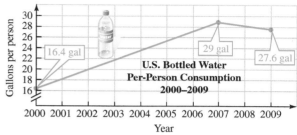

Source: beveragemarketing.com

SECTION 5.6

Slope–Intercept Form

Objectives

1 Use slope–intercept form to identify the slope and y-intercept of a line.

2 Write a linear equation in slope–intercept form.

3 Write an equation of a line given its slope and y-intercept.

4 Use the slope and y-intercept to graph a linear equation.

5 Recognize parallel and perpendicular lines.

6 Use slope–intercept form to write an equation to model data.

ARE YOU READY?

The following problems review some basic skills that are needed to find the slope of a line.

1. a. Identify each term in the expression $3x - 6$.

   b. What is the coefficient of the first term?

2. Solve for y: $2x + 5y = 15$

3. True or false: $\dfrac{x}{4} = \dfrac{1}{4}x$

4. Write 3 as a fraction.

5. On what axis does the point $(0, 6)$ lie?

6. True or false: $-\dfrac{7}{8} = \dfrac{-7}{8} = \dfrac{7}{-8}$

Of all the ways in which a linear equation can be written, one form, called *slope–intercept form,* is probably the most useful. When an equation is written in this form, two important features of its graph are evident.

1 **Use slope–intercept form to identify the slope and y-intercept of a line.**

The graph of $y = -\frac{2}{3}x + 4$ shown in the figure on the next page enables us to see that the slope of the line is $-\frac{2}{3}$ and that the y-intercept is $(0, 4)$.

$$y = -\frac{2}{3}x + 4$$

x	y	(x, y)
0	4	$(0, 4)$
3	2	$(3, 2)$

↓

To find the slope of the line, we pick two points on the line, (0, 4) and (3, 2); draw a slope triangle; and count grid squares:

$$\text{slope} = \frac{\text{rise}}{\text{run}} = \frac{-2}{3} = -\frac{2}{3}$$

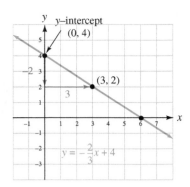

From the equation and the graph, we can make two observations:

- The graph crosses the y-axis at 4. This is the same as the constant term in $y = -\frac{2}{3}x + 4$
- The slope of the line is $-\frac{2}{3}$. This is the same as the coefficient of x in $y = -\frac{2}{3}x + 4$

$$y = -\frac{2}{3}x + 4$$
↑   ↑

The slope   The y-intercept
of the line.   is (0, 4).
is $-\frac{2}{3}$.

These observations suggest the following form of an equation of a line.

Slope-Intercept Form of the Equation of a Line

If a linear equation is written in the form

$$y = mx + b$$

the graph of the equation is a line with slope m and y-intercept $(0, b)$.

Self Check 1

Find the slope and the y-intercept:

a. $y = -5x - 1$

b. $y = \frac{7}{8}x$

c. $y = 5 - \frac{x}{3}$

Now Try Problems 21 and 23

EXAMPLE 1   Find the slope and the y-intercept of the graph of each equation:

a. $y = 6x - 2$ **b.** $y = -\frac{5}{4}x$ **c.** $y = \frac{x}{2} + 6$

Strategy We will write each equation in slope–intercept form, $y = mx + b$.

WHY When the linear equations are written in slope–intercept form, the slope and the y-intercept of their graphs become apparent.

Solution

a. If we write the subtraction as the addition of the opposite, the equation will be in $y = mx + b$ form:

$$y = 6x + (-2)$$

Since $m = 6$ and $b = -2$, the slope of the line is 6 and the y-intercept is $(0, -2)$.

b. Writing $y = -\frac{5}{4}x$ in slope–intercept form, we have

$$y = -\frac{5}{4}x + 0$$

Since $m = -\frac{5}{4}$ and $b = 0$, the slope of the line is $-\frac{5}{4}$ and the y-intercept is $(0, 0)$.

c. Since $\frac{x}{2}$ means $\frac{1}{2}x$, we can rewrite $y = \frac{x}{2} + 6$ as

$$y = \frac{1}{2}x + 6$$

We see that $m = \frac{1}{2}$ and $b = 6$, so the slope of the line is $\frac{1}{2}$ and the y-intercept is $(0, 6)$.

Caution! If a linear equation is written in the form $y = mx + b$, the slope of the graph is the *coefficient* of x, not the term involving x. For example, it would be incorrect to say that the graph of $y = 5x + 1$ has a slope of $m = 5x$. Its graph has slope $m = 5$.

THINK IT THROUGH *Prospects for a Teaching Career*

"Teachers who are geographically mobile and who obtain qualifications in more than one subject are likely to have a distinct advantage in finding a job."
Bureau of Labor Statistics, Occupational Outlook Handbook, 2010-2011

Have you ever thought about becoming a teacher? There will be plenty of openings in the future, especially for mathematics and science teachers. The equation

$$y = 1{,}247x + 17{,}450$$

approximates the average teacher salary y, where x is the number of years after 1980. Graph the equation. What information about teacher salaries is given by the slope of the line? By the y-intercept? What is the predicted average teacher salary 5 years from now? *(Source: U.S. Bureau of the Census, National Center for Education Statistics)*

---

2 **Write a linear equation in slope–intercept form.**

The equation of any nonvertical line can be written in slope–intercept form. To do so, we apply the properties of equality to solve the equation for y.

EXAMPLE 2 Find the slope and the y-intercept of the line determined by $6x - 3y = 9$.

Strategy We will use the properties of equality to write each equation in slope–intercept form, $y = mx + b$.

WHY When the linear equations are written in slope–intercept form, the slope and the y-intercept of their graphs become apparent.

Solution
To find the slope and the y-intercept of the line, we write the equation in slope–intercept form by solving for y.

$$6x - 3y = 9$$
$$-3y = -6x + 9 \qquad \text{Subtract } 6x \text{ from both sides.}$$

Self Check 2
Find the slope and the y-intercept of the line determined by $8x - 2y = -2$.

Now Try Problem 29

$$\frac{-3y}{-3} = \frac{-6x}{-3} + \frac{9}{-3}$$ To undo the multiplication by −3, divide both sides by −3. On the right-hand side, dividing each term by −3 is equivalent to dividing the entire side by −3: $\frac{-6x+9}{-3} = \frac{-6x}{-3} + \frac{9}{-3}$

$$y = 2x - 3$$ Perform the divisions. Here, $m = 2$ and $b = -3$.

From the equation, we see that the slope is 2 and the *y*-intercept is $(0, -3)$.

3 Write an equation of a line given its slope and *y*-intercept.

If we are given the slope and *y*-intercept of a line, we can write an equation of the line by substituting for *m* and *b* in the slope-intercept form.

Self Check 3

Write an equation of the line with slope 1 and *y*-intercept $(0, -12)$.

Now Try **Problem 33**

EXAMPLE 3 Write an equation of the line with slope −1 and *y*-intercept (0, 9).

Strategy We will use the slope–intercept form, $y = mx + b$, to write an equation of the line.

WHY We know the slope of the line and its *y*-intercept.

Solution

If the slope is −1 and the *y*-intercept is (0, 9), then $m = -1$ and $b = 9$.

$y = mx + b$ This is the slope–intercept form.

$y = -1x + 9$ Substitute −1 for *m* and 9 for *b*.

$y = -x + 9$ Simplify: $-1x = -1$.

The equation of the line with slope −1 and *y*-intercept (0, 9) is $y = -x + 9$.

Self Check 4

Write an equation of the line graphed here.

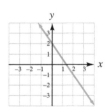

Now Try **Problem 37**

EXAMPLE 4 Write an equation of the line graphed in figure (a).

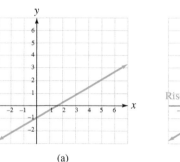

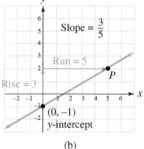

(a) (b)

Pick a second point on the line that lies on the intersection of two grid lines.

Strategy We will use the slope–intercept form, $y = mx + b$, to write an equation of the line.

WHY We can determine the slope and *y*-intercept of the line from the given graph.

Solution

In figure (b), we highlight and label the *y*-intercept of the line, (0, −1). Then we pick a convenient second point on the line and label it point P. Moving from the *y*-intercept to point P, we draw a slope triangle to find that the slope of the line is $\frac{3}{5}$. When we substitute $\frac{3}{5}$ for *m* and −1 for *b* into the slope–intercept form $y = mx + b$, we obtain an equation of the line: $y = \frac{3}{5}x - 1$.

4 Use the slope and *y*-intercept to graph a linear equation.

To graph $y = 2x - 3$, we plot the *y*-intercept $(0, -3)$, as shown. Since the slope is $\frac{\text{rise}}{\text{run}} = 2 = \frac{2}{1}$, the line rises 2 units for every unit it moves to the right. If we begin at $(0, -3)$ and move 2 units up (rise) and then 1 unit to the right (run), we locate the point $(1, -1)$, which is a second point on the line. We then draw a line through $(0, -3)$ and $(1, -1)$.

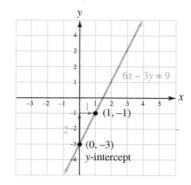

5 Recognize parallel and perpendicular lines.

The slope–intercept form enables us to quickly identify parallel and perpendicular lines.

EXAMPLE 5   Determine whether the graphs of $y = -\dfrac{2}{3}x$ and $y = -\dfrac{2}{3}x + 3$ are parallel, perpendicular, or neither.

Strategy We will find the slope of each line and compare the slopes.

WHY If the slopes are equal, the lines are parallel. If the slopes are negative reciprocals, the lines are perpendicular. Otherwise, the lines are neither parallel nor perpendicular.

Solution
The graph of $y = -\frac{2}{3}x$ is a line with slope $-\frac{2}{3}$. The graph of $y = -\frac{2}{3}x + 3$ is a line with slope of $-\frac{2}{3}$. Since the slopes $-\frac{2}{3}$ and $-\frac{2}{3}$ are the same, the lines are parallel. ■

Self Check 5

Determine whether the graphs of $y = -\frac{3}{2}x + 1$ and $y = \frac{3}{2}x + 4$ are parallel, perpendicular, or neither.

Now Try **Problems 45 and 46**

EXAMPLE 6   Are the graphs of $y = -5x + 6$ and $x - 5y = -10$ parallel, perpendicular, or neither?

Strategy We will find the slope of each line and then compare the slopes.

WHY If the slopes are equal, the lines are parallel. If the slopes are negative reciprocals, the lines are perpendicular. Otherwise, the lines are neither parallel nor perpendicular.

Solution
The graph of $y = -5x + 6$ is a line with slope -5. To find the slope of the graph of $x - 5y = -10$, we will write the equation in slope–intercept form.

$$x - 5y = -10$$
$$-5y = -x - 10 \qquad \textit{To eliminate x from the left side, subtract x from both sides.}$$
$$\frac{-5y}{-5} = \frac{-x}{-5} - \frac{10}{-5} \qquad \textit{To isolate y, undo the multiplication by −5 by dividing both sides by −5.}$$
$$y = \frac{x}{5} + 2 \qquad \textit{m} = \tfrac{1}{5} \textit{ because } \tfrac{x}{5} = \tfrac{1}{5}x.$$

The graph of $y = \frac{x}{5} + 2$ is a line with slope $\frac{1}{5}$. Since the slopes -5 and $\frac{1}{5}$ are negative reciprocals, the lines are perpendicular. This is verified by the fact that the product of their slopes is -1.

$$-5\left(\frac{1}{5}\right) = -\frac{5}{5} = -1$$

Self Check 6

Determine whether the graphs of $y = 4x + 6$ and $x - 4y = -8$ are parallel, perpendicular, or neither.

Now Try **Problem 49**

> **Success Tip**   Graphs are not necessary to determine if two lines are parallel, perpendicular, or neither. We simply examine the slopes of the lines.

6   Use slope–intercept form to write an equation to model data.

The concepts that we have studied in sections 2 through 5 of this module can be used to write equations that mathematically describe, or **model**, many real-world situations.

Self Check 7

COLLEGE FEES Each semester, students enrolling at a community college must pay tuition costs of $45 per unit as well as a basic $75 students services fee. Write a linear equation that gives the total fees *y* to be paid by a student enrolling at the college and taking *x* units.

Now Try **Problem 77**

EXAMPLE 7   *Limo Service*   On weekends, a limousine service charges a fee of $100, plus 50¢ per mile, for the rental of a stretch limo. Write a linear equation that describes the relationship between the rental cost and the number of miles driven. Graph the result.

Strategy We will determine the slope and the *y*-intercept of the graph of the equation from the given facts about the limo service.

WHY If we know the slope and *y*-intercept, we can use the slope–intercept form, $y = mx + b$, to write the equation to model the situation.

Solution

To write an equation describing this relationship, we will let *x* represent the number of miles driven and *y* represent the cost (in dollars). We can make two observations:

- The cost increases by 50¢ or $0.50 for each mile driven. This is the *rate of change* of the rental cost to miles driven, and it will be the *slope* of the graph of the equation. Thus, $m = 0.50$.
- The basic fee is $100. Before driving any miles (that is, when $x = 0$), the cost *y* is 100. The ordered pair (0, 100) will be the *y*-intercept of the graph of the equation. So we know that $b = 100$.

We substitute 0.50 for *m* and 100 for *b* in the slope–intercept form to get

$$y = 0.50x + 100 \qquad \text{Here the cost } y \text{ depends on } x, \text{ the number of miles driven.}$$
$$\uparrow\uparrow$$
$$m = 0.50b = 100$$

To graph $y = 0.50x + 100$, we plot its *y*-intercept, (0, 100). Since the slope is $0.50 = \frac{50}{100} = \frac{5}{10}$, we can start at (0, 100) and locate a second point on the line by moving 5 units up (rise) and then 10 units to the right (run). This point will have coordinates (0 + 10, 100 + 5) or (10, 105). We draw a straight line through these two points to get a graph that illustrates the relationship between the rental cost and the number of miles driven. We draw the graph only in quadrant I, because the number of miles driven is always positive.

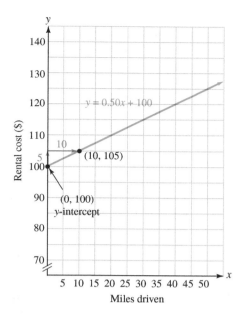

To make a linear model more descriptive of the given situation, we can replace the variables x and y in $y = mx + b$ with other letters.

EXAMPLE 8 *Group Discounts* To promote group sales for an Alaskan cruise, a travel agency reduces the regular ticket price of $4,500 by $5 for each person traveling in the group.

a. Write a linear equation that gives the per-person cost c of the cruise, if p people travel together.

b. Use the equation to determine the per-person cost if 55 teachers travel together.

Strategy We will determine the slope and the y-intercept of the graph of the equation from the given facts about the cruise.

WHY If we know the slope and y-intercept, we can use the slope–intercept form, $y = mx + b$, to write an equation to model the situation.

Solution

a. We will let p represent the number of people traveling in the group and c represent the per-person cost of the cruise. Since the cost depends on the number of people in the group, the linear equation that models this situation is

$$c = mp + b$$ This is the slope-intercept form $y = mx + b$ with the variable c in place of y and the variable p in place of x.

Since the per-person cost of the cruise steadily decreases as the number of people in the group increases, the rate of change of $-$\$5 per person is the slope of the graph of the equation. Thus, m is -5.

If 0 people take the cruise, there will be no discount and the per-person cost of the cruise will be $4,500. Written as an ordered pair of the form (p, c), we have $(0, 4,500)$. When graphed, this point would be the c-intercept. Thus, b is 4,500.

Cruise to Alaska
$4,500 per person
Group discounts available*

*For groups of up to 100

Self Check 8

GROUP DISCOUNTS Write a linear equation in slope–intercept form that gives the cost of the cruise of Example 8 if a $10.50-per-person discount is offered for groups.

Now Try Problem 84

Substituting for m and b in the slope–intercept form $c = mp + b$, we obtain the linear equation that models the pricing arrangement.

A graph of the equation for groups of up to 100 ($c \le 100$) is shown on the right.

$$c = -5p + 4{,}500 \quad \text{\small$m = -5$ and $b = 4{,}500$}$$

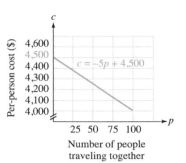

b. To find the per-person cost of the cruise for a group of 55 people, we substitute 55 for p and evaluate the right side of the equation.

$$c = -5p + 4{,}500$$
$$c = -5(55) + 4{,}500 \quad \text{\small Substitute 55 for p.}$$
$$c = -275 + 4{,}500 \quad \text{\small Do the multiplication.}$$
$$c = 4{,}225 \quad \text{\small Do the addition.}$$

If a group of 55 people travel together, the cruise will cost each person \$4,225. ■

The Language of Algebra

To determine the slope m for modeling problems like this, look for a phrase that describes a **rate of change,** such as:

- \$5 for each person
- \$20 per unit
- 5° every minute
- 12 feet a year

ANSWERS TO SELF CHECKS

1. a. $m = -5$, $(0, -1)$ **b.** $m = \frac{7}{8}$, $(0, 0)$ **c.** $m = -\frac{1}{3}$, $(0, 5)$ **2.** $m = 4$, $(0, 1)$
3. $y = x - 12$ **4.** $y = -\frac{3}{2}x + 2$ **5.** neither **6.** neither **7.** $y = 45x + 75$
8. $c = -10.50p + 4{,}500$

SECTION 5.6   STUDY SET

VOCABULARY

Fill in the blanks.

1. The equation $y = mx + b$ is called the _____ form for the equation of a line.

2. _____ lines do not intersect. _____ lines meet at right angles.

CONCEPTS

3. The graph of the linear equation $y = mx + b$ has _____ $(0, b)$ and _____ m.

4. The numbers $\frac{5}{6}$ and $-\frac{6}{5}$ are negative _____ because their product is -1.

5. Determine whether each equation is in slope–intercept form.
   a. $7x + 4y = 2$ **b.** $5y = 2x - 3$
   c. $y = 6x + 1$ **d.** $x = 4y - 8$

6. Determine the slope of the graph of each equation.
   a. $y = \dfrac{-2x}{3} - 2$ **b.** $y = \dfrac{x}{4} + 1$
   c. $y = 2 - 8x$ **d.** $y = 3x$
   e. $y = x$ **f.** $y = -x$

7. See the illustration.
   a. What is the slope of the line?
   b. What is the *y*-intercept of the line?
   c. Write the equation of the line.

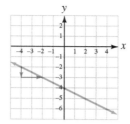

8. See the illustration.
   a. What is the slope of the line?
   b. What is the *y*-intercept of the line?
   c. Write the equation of the line.

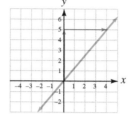

9. For the line in the illustration, find its slope and *y*-intercept. Then write the equation of the line in slope–intercept form by filling in the blanks:

$y = \boxed{} x + \boxed{}$.

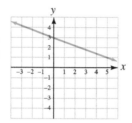

10. a. Fill in the blank: To write a linear equation in two variables in slope–intercept form, solve the equation for ☐.
    b. Solve $4x + y = 9$ for *y*.

11. Simplify the right side of each equation.
    a. $y = \dfrac{4x}{2} + \dfrac{16}{2}$
    b. $y = \dfrac{15x}{-3} + \dfrac{9}{-3}$
    c. $y = \dfrac{2x}{6} - \dfrac{6}{6}$
    d. $y = \dfrac{-9x}{-5} - \dfrac{20}{-5}$

12. a. What is the slope of a line that is parallel to the line represented by $y = 8x - 10$?
    b. What is the slope of a line that is perpendicular to the line represented by $y = \frac{3}{4}x - 6$?

13. In the illustration in the next column, the slope of line l_1 is 2.
    a. Determine the slope of line l_2.
    b. Determine the slope of line l_3.
    c. Determine the slope of line l_4.
    d. Which lines have the same *y*-intercept?

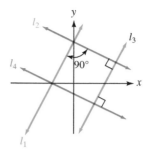

14. a. Determine the *y*-intercept of line l_1 in the illustration.

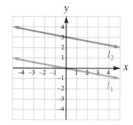

    b. What do lines l_1 and l_2 have in common? How are they different?

Without graphing, determine whether the graphs of each pair of lines are parallel, perpendicular, or neither.

15. $y = 0.5x - 3, y = \frac{1}{2}x + 3$
16. $y = 0.75x, y = -\frac{4}{3}x + 2$
17. $y = -x, y = -2x$
18. $y = \frac{2}{3}x - 4, y = -\frac{3}{2}x + 4$

▌ NOTATION

Complete the steps to solve the equation for y. Then find the slope and the y-intercept of its graph.

19.
$$6x - 2y = 10$$
$$6x - \boxed{} - 2y = -6x + 10$$
$$-2y = \boxed{} + 10$$
$$\frac{-2y}{\boxed{}} = \frac{-6x}{\boxed{}} + \frac{10}{\boxed{}}$$
$$y = \boxed{} - 5$$

The slope is ☐ and the *y*-intercept is ☐ .

20.
$$2x + 5y = 15$$
$$2x + 5y - \boxed{} = \boxed{} + 15$$
$$\boxed{} = -2x + 15$$
$$\frac{5y}{\boxed{}} = \frac{-2x}{\boxed{}} + \frac{15}{\boxed{}}$$
$$y = -\frac{2}{5}x + 3$$

The slope is ☐ and the *y*-intercept is ☐ .

GUIDED PRACTICE

Find the slope and the y-intercept of the graph of each equation.
See Examples 1.

21. $y = 4x + 2$

22. $y = -4x - 2$

23. $y = \dfrac{x}{4} - \dfrac{1}{2}$

24. $y = \dfrac{1}{2}x + 6$

Find the slope and the y-intercept of the graph of each equation.
See Examples 2.

25. $4x - 2 = y$

26. $6 - x = y$

27. $6y = x - 6$

28. $6x - 1 = y$

29. $4x - 3y = 12$

30. $2x + 3y = 6$

31. $10x - 5y = 12$

32. $7x + 4y = 16$

Write an equation of the line with the given slope and
y-intercept. **See Examples 3.**

33. Slope $\dfrac{1}{4}$, y-intercept $(0, -2)$

34. Slope $-\dfrac{7}{6}$, y-intercept $(0, 2)$

35. Slope $\dfrac{5}{4}$, y-intercept $(0, 0)$

36. Slope -3, y-intercept $\left(0, -\dfrac{1}{2}\right)$

Write an equation for each line shown below. **See Examples 4.**

37.

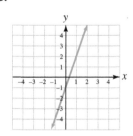

38.

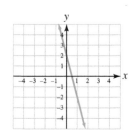

39.

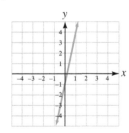

40.

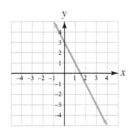

41.

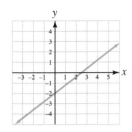

42.

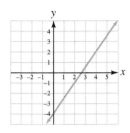

43.

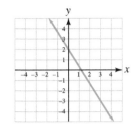

44.

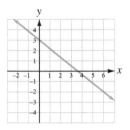

For each pair of equations, determine whether their graphs are
parallel, perpendicular, or neither. **See Examples 5 and 6.**

45. $y = 6x + 8$
   $y = 6x$

46. $y = 3x - 15$
   $y = -\dfrac{1}{3}x + 4$

47. $y = x$
   $y = -x$

48. $y = \dfrac{1}{2}x - \dfrac{4}{5}$
   $y = 0.5x + 3$

49. $y = -2x - 9$
   $2x - y = 9$

50. $y = \dfrac{3}{4}x + 1$
   $4x - 3y = 15$

51. $x - y = 12$
   $-2x + 2y = -23$

52. $x = 9$
   $y = 8$

TRY IT YOURSELF

Find the slope and the y-intercept of the graph of each equation.

53. $x + y = 8$

54. $x - y = -30$

55. $2x + 3y = 6$

56. $3x - 5y = 15$

57. $3y - 13 = 0$

58. $-5y - 2 = 0$

59. $y = -5x$

60. $y = 14x$

Write an equation of the line with the given slope and y-intercept. Then graph it.

61. $m = 5, (0, -3)$

62. $m = -2, (0, 1)$

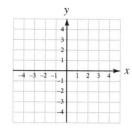
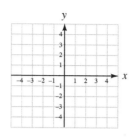

63. $m = \frac{1}{4}, (0, -2)$

64. $m = \frac{1}{3}, (0, -5)$

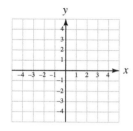
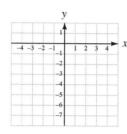

65. $m = -3, (0, 6)$

66. $m = 2, (0, 1)$

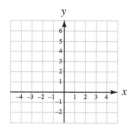
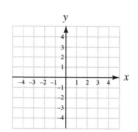

67. $m = -\frac{8}{3}, (0, 5)$

68. $m = -\frac{7}{6}, (0, 2)$

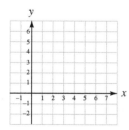
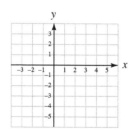

Find the slope and the y-intercept of the graph of each equation. Then graph it.

69. $y = 3x + 3$

70. $y = -3x + 5$

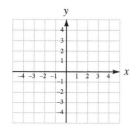
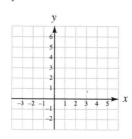

71. $y = -\frac{x}{2} + 2$

72. $y = \frac{x}{3}$

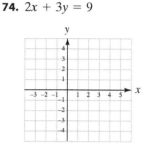
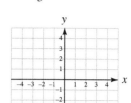

73. $3x + 4y = 16$

74. $2x + 3y = 9$

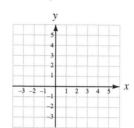
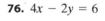

75. $10x - 5y = 5$

76. $4x - 2y = 6$

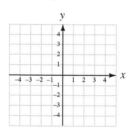
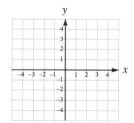

APPLICATIONS

77. PRODUCTION COSTS A television production company charges a basic fee of $5,000 and then $2,000 an hour when filming a commercial.

  a. Write a linear equation that describes the relationship between the total production costs y and the hours of filming x.

  b. Use your answer to part a to find the production costs if a commercial required 8 hours of filming.

78. COLLEGE FEES Each semester, students enrolling at a community college must pay tuition costs of $20 per unit as well as a $40 student services fee.

  a. Write a linear equation that gives the total fees y to be paid by a student enrolling at the college and taking x units.

  b. Use your answer to part a to find the enrollment cost for a student taking 12 units.

79. CHEMISTRY EXPERIMENT The following illustration shows a portion of a student's chemistry lab manual. Use the information to write a linear equation relating the temperature y (in degrees Fahrenheit) of the compound to the time x (in minutes) elapsed during the lab procedure.

> Chem. Lab #1   Aug. 13
> **Step 1:** Removed compound
> from freezer @ −10° F.
>
> **Step 2:** Used heating unit
> to raise temperature
> of compound 5° F
> every minute.

80. INCOME PROPERTY Use the information in the newspaper advertisement below to write a linear equation that gives the amount of income y (in dollars) the apartment owner will receive when the unit is rented for x months.

> **APARTMENT FOR RENT**
> 1 bedroom/1 bath,
> with garage
> $500 per month +
> $250 nonrefundable
> security fee.

81. SALAD BAR For lunch, a delicatessen offers a "Salad and Soda" special where customers serve themselves at a well-stocked salad bar. The cost is $1.00 for the drink and 20¢ an ounce for the salad.

   a. Write a linear equation that will find the cost y of a lunch when a salad weighing x ounces is purchased.

   b. Graph the equation using the grid in the next column.

   c. How would the graph from part b change if the delicatessen began charging $2.00 for the drink?

   d. How would the graph from part b change if the cost of the salad changed to 30¢ an ounce?

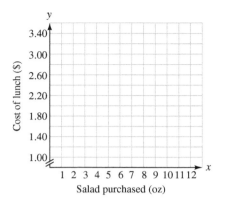

82. SEWING COSTS A tailor charges a basic fee of $20 plus $2.50 per letter to sew an athlete's name on the back of a jacket.

   a. Write a linear equation that will find the cost y to have a name containing x letters sewn on the back of a jacket.

   b. Graph the equation on the grid is shown below.

   c. Suppose the tailor raises the basic fee to $30. On your graph from part b, draw the new graph showing the increased cost.

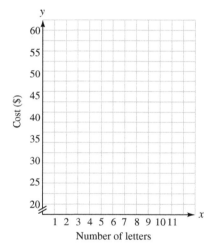

83. EMPLOYMENT SERVICE A policy statement of LIZCO, Inc., is shown below. Suppose a secretary had to pay an employment service $500 to get placed in a new job at LIZCO. Write a linear equation that tells the secretary the actual cost y of the employment service to her x months after being hired.

> **Policy no. 23452**– A new hire will be reimbursed by LIZCO for any employment service fees paid by the employee at the rate of $20 per month.

84. PRINTING PRESSES Every three minutes, 100 feet of paper is used off of an 8,000 foot-roll to print the pages of a magazine. Write a linear equation that relates the number of feet of paper that remain on the roll and the number of minutes the printing press has been operating.

85. IPADS When a student purchased an Apple iPad with Wi-Fi + 3G for $629.99, he also enrolled in a 250 MB data plan that cost $14.95 per month.

a. Write a linear equation that gives the cost for him to purchase and use the iPad for m months.

b. Use your answer to part a to find the cost to purchase and use the iPad for 2 years.

86. ONLINE GAMES A new Playstation 3 costs $310.50 and membership in an online videogame multiplayer network cost $18.49 per month.

a. Write a linear equation that gives the cost for someone to buy the machine and belong to the online network for m months.

b. Use your answer to part a to find the cost to buy the machine and belong to the network for 3 years.

87. NAVIGATION The graph below shows the recommended speed at which a ship should proceed into head waves of various heights.

a. What information does the y-intercept of the line give?

b. What is the rate of change in the recommended speed of the ship as the wave height increases?

c. Write an equation of the line.

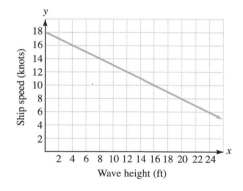

88. DEBT The graph in the next column estimates the amount of credit card debt per U.S. household for the years 1990–2010.

a. What information does the d-intercept of the line give?

b. What was the rate of change in the amount of debt per household?

c. Write an equation of the line, where d is the approximate credit card debt and t is the number of years since 1990.

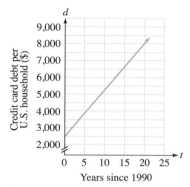

Source: mybudget 360.com

89. ALASKAN OIL According to the U.S. Energy Information Administration, in 1990, about 650,000,000 barrels of crude oil were produced from drilling in Alaska. Since then, the annual production has decreased by about 22,000,000 per year.

a. Write a linear model in slope–intercept form that gives the number of barrels b of crude oil produced in Alaska t years after 1990.

b. If the equation were graphed, what would be the meaning of the b-intercept and the slope of the line?

90. COMPUTER DRAFTING The illustration below shows a computer-generated drawing of an automobile engine mount. When the designer clicks the mouse on a line of the drawing, the computer finds the equation of the line. Determine whether the two lines selected in the drawing are perpendicular.

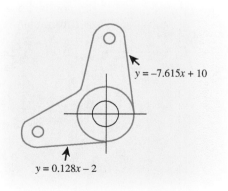

WRITING

91. Explain the advantages of writing the equation of a line in slope–intercept form ($y = mx + b$) as opposed to general form ($Ax + By = C$).

92. Why is $y = mx + b$ called the slope–intercept form of the equation of a line?

93. What is the minimum number of points needed to draw the graph of a line? Explain why.

94. List some examples of parallel and perpendicular lines that you see in your daily life.

95. On a quiz, a student was asked to find the slope of the graph of $y = 2x + 3$. She answered: $m = 2x$. Her instructor marked it wrong. Explain why the answer is incorrect.

96. a. Suppose you know the slope of a line. Is that enough information about the line to write its equation? Explain.
   b. Suppose you know the y-intercept of a line. Is that enough information about the line to write its equation? Explain.

Objectives

1 Use point-slope form to write an equation of a line.

2 Write an equation of a line given two points on the line.

3 Write equations of horizontal and vertical lines.

4 Use a point and the slope to graph a line.

5 Write linear equations that model data.

SECTION **5.7**

Point-Slope Form

ARE YOU READY?

The following problems review some basic skills that are needed when working with equations of lines in point-slope form.

1. Find the slope of the line that passes through $(-2, 0)$ and $(-12, -8)$.

2. Simplify: $x - (-5)$

3. Solve $y + 2 = 6(x - 7)$ for y.

4. Add: $-\dfrac{3}{4} + 8$

If we know the slope of a line and its y-intercept, we can use the slope–intercept form to write the equation of the line. The question that now arises is, can *any* point on the line be used in combination with its slope to write its equation? In this section, we answer this question.

1 **Use point–slope form to write an equation of a line.**

Refer to the line graphed on the left, with slope 3 and passing through the point $(2, 1)$. To develop a new form for the equation of a line, we will find the slope of this line in another way.

    If we pick another point on the line with coordinates (x, y), we can find the slope of the line by substituting the coordinates of the points (x, y) and $(2, 1)$ into the slope formula.

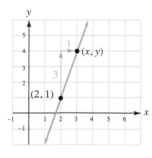

$$\frac{y_2 - y_1}{x_2 - x_1} = m$$

$$\frac{y - 1}{x - 2} = m \qquad \text{Let } (x_1, y_1) \text{ be } (2, 1) \text{ and } (x_2, y_2) \text{ be } (x, y).$$
$$\text{Substitute } y \text{ for } y_2, 1 \text{ for } y_1, x \text{ for } x_2, \text{ and } 2 \text{ for } x_1.$$

Since the slope of the line is 3, we can substitute 3 for in the previous equation.

$$\frac{y - 1}{x - 2} = 3$$

We then multiply both sides by $x - 2$ to clear the equation of the fraction.

$$\frac{y - 1}{x - 2}(x - 2) = 3(x - 2)$$

$y - 1 = 3(x - 2)$ Simplify the left side. Remove the common factor $x - 2$ in

the numerator and denominator: $\frac{y-1}{x-2} \cdot \frac{x-2}{1}$.

The resulting equation displays the slope of the line and the coordinates of one point on the line:

Slope of the line
↓
$$y - 1 = 3(x - 2)$$
↑ ↑
y-coordinate of the point   x-coordinate of the point

In general, suppose we know that the slope of a line is m and that the line passes through the point (x_1, y_1). Then if (x, y) is any other point on the line, we can use the definition of slope to write

$$\frac{y - y_1}{x - x_1} = m$$

If we multiply both sides by $x - x_1$ to clear the equation of the fraction, we have

$y - y_1 = m(x - x_1)$

This form of a linear equation is called **point–slope form.** It can be used to write the equation of a line when the slope and one point on the line are known.

Point-Slope Form of the Equation of a Line

If a line with slope m passes through the point (x_1, y_1), the equation of the line is

$y - y_1 = m(x - x_1)$ Read as "y minus y sub 1 equals m times the quantity x minus x sub 1."

EXAMPLE 1   Find an equation of a line that has slope -8 and passes through $(-1, 5)$. Write the answer in slope–intercept form.

Strategy Although the problem asks for an answer in slope–intercept form, we will begin with the point–slope form to write an equation of the line.

WHY We know the slope of the line and the coordinates of a point that it passes through.

Solution
The given point is $(-1, 5)$, so $x_1 = -1$ and $y_1 = 5$. The given slope is -8, so $m = -8$. We will substitute these values into the point–slope form and simplify the right side of the equation.

$y - y_1 = m(x - x_1)$ This is the point–slope form.

$y - 5 = -8[x - (-1)]$ Substitute -8 for m, -1 for x_1, and 5 for y_1.
                          Brackets are used to enclose $x - (-1)$.

$y - 5 = -8(x + 1)$ Simplify the expression within the brackets.

To write an equivalent equation in slope–intercept form, we solve for y.

$y - 5 = -8(x + 1)$ This is the simplified point–slope form.

$y - 5 = -8x - 8$ Distribute the multiplication by -8.

Self Check 1

Find an equation of the line that has slope -2 and passes through $(4, -3)$. Write the answer in slope–intercept form.

Now Try Problems 13 and 19

$$y - 5 + 5 = -8x - 8 + 5 \quad \text{To isolate } y, \text{ undo the subtraction}$$
$$\text{of 5 by adding 5 to both sides.}$$

$$y = -8x - 3 \quad \text{This is the requested slope–intercept form.}$$

In slope–intercept form, the equation is $y = -8x - 3$.

To verify this result, we note that $m = -8$. Therefore, the slope of the line is -8, as required. To see whether the line passes through $(-1, 5)$, we substitute -1 for x and 5 for y in the equation. If this point is on the line, a true statement should result.

$$y = -8x - 3$$
$$5 \overset{?}{=} -8(-1) - 3$$
$$5 \overset{?}{=} 8 - 3$$
$$5 = 5 \quad \text{True}$$

Caution!   When using the point-slope form, never substitute values for x or y.
$$y - y_1 = m(x - x_1)$$
Only substitute values for $x_1, y_1,$ and m.

---

2 **Write an equation of a line given two points on the line.**

In the next example, we show that it is possible to write the equation of a line when we know the coordinates of two points on the line.

Self Check 2

Find an equation of the line that passes through $(-5, 4)$ and $(8, -6)$. Write the equation in slope–intercept form.

***Now Try* Problem 29**

EXAMPLE 2   Find an equation of the line that passes through $(-2, 6)$ and $(4, 7)$. Write the equation in slope–intercept form.

Strategy We will use the point–slope form, $y - y_1 = m(x - x_1)$, to write an equation of the line.

WHY We know the coordinates of a point that the line passes through and we can calculate the slope of the line using the slope formula.

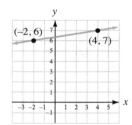

Solution
To find the slope of the line, we use the slope formula.

$$m = \frac{y_2 - y_1}{x_2 - x_1} = \frac{7 - 6}{4 - (-2)} = \frac{1}{6} \quad \text{Substitute 7 for } y_2, \text{ 6 for } y_1, \text{ 4 for } x_2, \text{ and } -2 \text{ for } x_1.$$

Either point on the line can serve as (x_1, y_1). The results will be the same. If we use $(4, 7)$, we have

$$y - y_1 = m(x - x_1) \quad \text{This is the point–slope form.}$$
$$y - 7 = \frac{1}{6}(x - 4) \quad \text{Substitute } \tfrac{1}{6} \text{ for } m, \text{ 7 for } y_1, \text{ and 4 for } x_1.$$

To write an equivalent equation in slope–intercept form, we solve for y.

$$y - 7 = \frac{1}{6}x - \frac{2}{3} \quad \text{Distribute the multiplication by } \tfrac{1}{6}: \tfrac{1}{6}(-4) = -\tfrac{4}{6} = -\tfrac{2}{3}.$$

$$y - 7 + 7 = \frac{1}{6}x - \frac{2}{3} + 7 \quad \text{To isolate } y, \text{ add 7 to both sides.}$$

$$y = \frac{1}{6}x - \frac{2}{3} + \frac{21}{3} \quad \text{Simplify the left side. On the right side, express 7 as } \tfrac{21}{3} \text{ to prepare to add the fractions with the common denominator 3.}$$

$$y = \frac{1}{6}x + \frac{19}{3}$$ *Add the fractions:* $-\frac{2}{3} + \frac{21}{3} = \frac{19}{3}$. *This is slope–intercept form.*

An equation of the line that passes through $(-2, 6)$ and $(4, 7)$ is $y = \frac{1}{6}x + \frac{19}{3}$.

Success Tip   To check this result, verify that $(-2, 6)$ and $(4, 7)$ satisfy the equation using substitution.

3 Write equations of horizontal and vertical lines.

We have previously graphed horizontal and vertical lines. We will now discuss how to write their equations.

EXAMPLE 3   Write an equation of each line and graph it. **a.** A horizontal line that passes through $(-2, -4)$ **b.** A vertical line that passes through $(1, 3)$

Strategy We will use the appropriate form, either $y = b$ or $x = a$, to write an equation of each line.

WHY These are the standard forms for the equations of a horizontal and a vertical line.

Solution

a. The equation of a horizontal line can be written in the form $y = b$. Since the y-coordinate of $(-2, -4)$ is -4, the equation of the line is $y = -4$. The graph is shown in the figure.

b. The equation of a vertical line can be written in the form $x = a$. Since the x-coordinate of $(1, 3)$ is 1, the equation of the line is $x = 1$. The graph is shown in the figure.

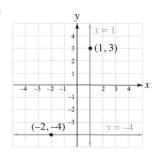

Self Check 3

Write an equation of each line.
a. A horizontal line that passes through $(3, 2)$
b. A vertical line passing through $(-1, -3)$

Now Try Problems 41 and 43

4 Use a point and the slope to graph a line.

If we know the coordinates of a point on a line, and if we know the slope of the line, we can use the slope to determine a second point on the line.

EXAMPLE 4   Graph the line with slope $\frac{2}{5}$ that passes through $(-1, -3)$.

Strategy First, we will plot the given point $(-1, -3)$. Then we will use the slope to find a second point that the line passes through.

WHY Once we determine two points that the line passes through, we can draw the graph of the line.

Solution

To draw the graph, we begin by plotting the point $(-1, -3)$. From there, we move 2 units up (rise) and then 5 units to the right (run), since the slope is $\frac{2}{5}$. This locates a second point on the line, $(4, -1)$. We then draw a straight line through the two points.

Self Check 4

Graph the line with slope -4 that passes through $(-4, 2)$.

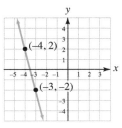

Now Try Problem 45

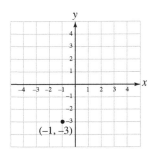

Plot the given point (−1, −3).

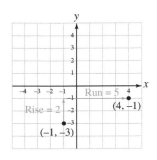

From (−1, −3) draw the rise and run parts of the slope triangle for $m = \frac{2}{5}$ to find another point on the line.

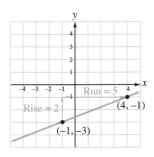

Use a straightedge to draw a line through the points.

The following table summarizes what you should know about each form of an equation of a line.

Form	Example	Comments
Standard form $Ax + By = C$	$2x + 5y = 9$	• To graph, find the *x*- and *y*-intercepts by letting $y = 0$ and finding *x*, and letting $x = 0$ and finding *y*. Also find a checkpoint.
Slope–intercept form $y = mx + b$	$y = \frac{5}{3}x + 4$	• To graph, plot the *y*-intercept $(0, b)$. From there, draw a slope triangle using the rise and run to locate another point. • Use this form to write a line's equation if you know its slope and *y*-intercept.
Point–slope form $y - y_1 = m(x - x_1)$	$y - 1 = 6(x - 8)$	• To graph, plot the point (x_1, y_1). From there, draw a slope triangle using the rise and run of the slope *m* to locate another point. • Use this form to write a line's equation if you know a point on the line and the slope. If two points on the line are known, find the slope and use it with one of the points to write the equation.
Horizontal line $y = b$	$y = 7$	• To graph, draw a horizontal line ($m = 0$) with *y*-intercept $(0, b)$.
Vertical line $x = a$	$x = -1$	• To graph, draw a vertical line (undefined slope) with *x*-intercept $(a, 0)$.

5 Write linear equations that model data.

In the next two examples, we will see how the point–slope form can be used to write linear equations that model certain real–world situations.

EXAMPLE 5   *Men's Shoe Sizes* The length (in inches) of a man's foot is not his shoe size. For example, the smallest adult men's shoe size is 5, and it fits a 9-inch-long foot. There is, however, a linear relationship between the two. It can be stated this way: Shoe size increases by 3 sizes for each 1-inch increase in foot length.

a. Write a linear equation that relates shoe size *s* to foot length *L*.
b. Shaquille O'Neal, a famous basketball player, has a foot that is about 14.6 inches long. Find his shoe size.

Strategy We will first find the slope of the line that describes the linear relationship between shoe size and the length of a foot. Then we will determine the coordinates of a point on that line.

WHY Once we know the slope and the coordinates of one point on the line, we can use the point–slope form to write the equation of the line.

Solution

a. Since shoe size *s* depends on the length *L* of the foot, ordered pairs have the form (*L*, *s*). Because the relationship is linear, the graph of the desired equation is a line.

- The line's slope is the rate of change: $\frac{3 \text{ sizes}}{1 \text{ inch}}$. Therefore, $m = 3$.
- A 9-inch-long foot wears size 5, so the line passes through (9, 5).

We substitute 3 for *m* and the coordinates of the point into the point–slope form and solve for *s*.

$s - s_1 = m(L - L_1)$ This is the point–slope form using the variables L and s.

$s - 5 = 3(L - 9)$ Substitute 3 for m, 9 for L_1, and 5 for s_1.

$s - 5 = 3L - 27$ Distribute the multiplication by 3.

$s = 3L - 22$ To isolate s, add 5 to both sides: $-27 + 5 = -22$.

The equation relating men's shoe size and foot length is $s = 3L - 22$.

b. To find Shaquille's shoe size, we substitute 14.6 inches for *L* in the equation.

$s = 3L - 22$

$s = 3(14.6) - 22$

$s = 43.8 - 22$ Do the multiplication.

$s = 21.8$ Do the subtraction.

Since men's shoes come in only full- and half-sizes, we round 21.8 up to 22. Shaquille O'Neal wears size 22 shoes.

Self Check 5

COMPARING TEMPERATURE SCALES
Celsius and Fahrenheit measures of temperature are not the same. There is, however, a linear relationship between the two. Degrees Fahrenheit increase by 9° for each 5° increase in Celsius. If a 212° Fahrenheit temperature measure is the same as 100° Celsius, write a linear equation that relates Fahrenheit measure to Celsius measure.

Now Try **Problem 77**

EXAMPLE 6   *Studying Learning*   In a series of 40 trials, a rat was released in a maze to search for food. Researchers recorded the trial number and the time that it took the rat to complete the maze as ordered pairs on a **scatter diagram** shown below. All of the points fell on or near the line drawn in red. Write an equation of the line in slope–intercept form.

Self Check 6

AWARDS Orders for awards to be given to math team members were placed on two separate occasions. The first order of 32 awards cost $172 and the second order of 5 awards cost $37. Write a linear equation that gives the cost for an order of any number of awards.

Now Try **Problem 85**

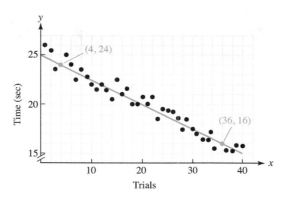

Strategy From the graph, we will determine the coordinates of two points on the line.

WHY We can write an equation of a line when we know the coordinates of two points on the line. (See Example 2.)

Solution

To write a point–slope equation, we need to know the slope of the line. The line passes through several points; we will use (4, 24) and (36, 16) to find its slope.

$$m = \frac{y_2 - y_1}{x_2 - x_1} = \frac{16 - 24}{36 - 4} = \frac{-8}{32} = -\frac{1}{4}$$

Any point on the line can serve as (x_1, y_1). We will use $(4, 24)$.

$$y - y_1 = m(x - x_1)$$ This is the point–slope form.

$$y - 24 = -\frac{1}{4}(x - 4)$$ Substitute $-\frac{1}{4}$ for m, 4 for x_1, and 24 for y_1.

To write this equation in slope–intercept form, solve for y.

$$y - 24 = -\frac{1}{4}x + 1$$ Distribute the multiplication by $-\frac{1}{4}$: $-\frac{1}{4}(-4) = 1$.

$$y = -\frac{1}{4}x + 25$$ To isolate y, add 24 to both sides: $1 + 24 = 25$.

A linear equation that models the rat's performance on the maze is $y = -\frac{1}{4}x + 25$, where x is the number of the trial and y is the time it took, in seconds.

The Language of Algebra

The term *scatter diagram* is somewhat misleading. Often, the data points are not scattered loosely about. In this case, they fall, more or less, along an imaginary straight line, indicating a linear relationship.

ANSWERS TO SELF CHECKS

1. $y = -2x + 5$ **2.** $y = -\frac{10}{13}x + \frac{2}{13}$ **3. a.** $y = 2$ **b.** $x = -1$ **4.**
5. $F = \frac{9}{5}C + 32$ **6.** $C = 5n + 12$

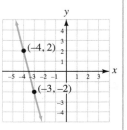

SECTION 5.7   STUDY SET

VOCABULARY

Fill in the blanks.

1. $y - y_1 = m(x - x_1)$ is called the _____ form of the equation of a line. In words, we read this as y minus y ____ one equals m _____ the quantity of x _____ x sub ____.

2. $y = mx + b$ is called the _____ form of the equation of a line.

CONCEPTS

3. Determine in what form each equation is written.
   a. $y - 4 = 2(x - 5)$
   b. $y = 2x + 15$

4. What point does the graph of each equation pass through, and what is the line's slope?

   a. $y - 2 = 6(x - 7)$
   b. $y + 3 = -8(x + 1)$

5. Refer to the following graph of a line.
   a. What highlighted point does the line pass through?
   b. What is the slope of the line?
   c. Write an equation of the line in point–slope form.

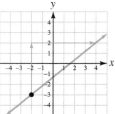

6. On a quiz, a student was asked to write the equation of a line with slope 4 that passes through $(-1, 3)$. Explain how the student can check her answer, $y = 4x + 7$.

7. Suppose you are asked to write an equation of the line in the scatter diagram below. What two points would you use to write the point–slope equation?

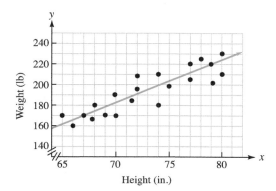

Height (in.)

8. In each case, a linear relationship between two quantities is described. If the relationship were graphed, what would be the slope of the line?

  a. The sales of new cars increased by 15 every 2 months.

  b. There were 35 fewer robberies for each dozen police officers added to the force.

  c. One acre of forest is being destroyed every 30 seconds.

NOTATION

Complete each step.

9. Find an equation of the line with slope -2 that passes through the point $(-1, 5)$. Write the answer in slope–intercept form.

$$y - y_1 = m(x - x_1)$$
$$y - \boxed{} = -2[x - (\boxed{})]$$
$$y - 5 = -2[x \boxed{} 1]$$
$$y - 5 = -2x - \boxed{}$$
$$y = -2x + \boxed{}$$

10. What is the point–slope form of the equation of a line?

11. Consider the steps below and then fill in the blanks:

$$y - 3 = 2(x + 1)$$
$$y - 3 = 2x + 2$$
$$y = 2x + 5$$

The original equation was in _____ form. After solving for y, we obtain an equation in _____ form.

12. Fill in the blanks: The equation of a horizontal line has the form $\boxed{} = b$ and the equation of a vertical line has the form $\boxed{} = a$.

GUIDED PRACTICE

Use the point–slope form to write an equation of the line with the given slope and point. Leave the equation in that form. **See Example 1.**

13. Slope 3, passes through $(2, 1)$

14. Slope 2, passes through $(4, 3)$

15. Slope $\dfrac{4}{5}$, passes through $(-5, -1)$

16. Slope $\dfrac{7}{8}$, passes through $(-2, -9)$

Use the point–slope form to find an equation of the line with the given slope and point. Then write the equation in slope–intercept form. **See Example 1.**

17. Slope 2, passes through $(3, 5)$

18. Slope 8, passes through $(2, 6)$

19. Slope -5, passes through $(-9, 8)$

20. Slope -4, passes through $(-2, 10)$

21. Slope -3, passes through the origin

22. Slope -1, passes through the origin

23. Slope $\dfrac{1}{5}$, passes through $(10, 1)$

24. Slope $\dfrac{1}{4}$, passes through $(8, 1)$

25. Slope $-\dfrac{4}{3}$,

x	y
-4	3
2	0

26. Slope $-\dfrac{3}{2}$,

x	y
-1	-4
1	-2

27. Slope $-\dfrac{11}{6}$, passes through $(2, -6)$

28. Slope $-\dfrac{5}{4}$, passes through $(2, 0)$

Find an equation of the line that passes through the two given points. Write the equation in slope–intercept form, if possible. **See Example 2.**

29. Passes through $(1, 7)$ and $(-2, 1)$

30. Passes through $(-2, 2)$ and $(2, -8)$

31.

x	y
6	-4

32.

x	y
-2	1

33. Passes through $(5, 5)$ and $(7, 5)$

34. Passes through $(-2, 1)$ and $(-2, 15)$

35. Passes through $(5, 1)$ and $(-5, 0)$

36. Passes through $(-3, 0)$ and $(3, 1)$

37. Passes through $(-8, 2)$ and $(-8, 17)$

38. Passes through $\left(\dfrac{2}{3}, 2\right)$ and $(0, 2)$

39. Passes through $\left(\frac{2}{3}, \frac{1}{3}\right)$ and $(0, 0)$

40. Passes through $\left(\frac{1}{2}, \frac{3}{4}\right)$ and $(0, 0)$

Write an equation of each line. **See Example 3.**

41. Vertical, passes through $(4, 5)$

42. Vertical, passes through $(-2, -5)$

43. Horizontal, passes through $(4, 5)$

44. Horizontal, passes through $(-2, -5)$

Graph the line that passes through the given point and has the given slope. **See Example 4.**

45. $(1, -2), m = -1$ **46.** $(-4, 1), m = -3$

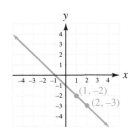   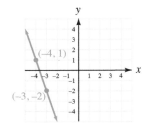

47. $(5, -3), \ m = \dfrac{3}{4}$ **48.** $(2, -4), \ m = \dfrac{2}{3}$

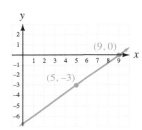   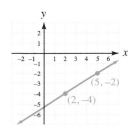

49. $(-2, -3),$ slope 2 **50.** $(-3, -3),$ slope 4

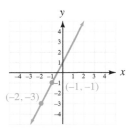   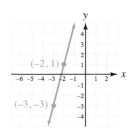

51. $(4, -3),$ slope $-\dfrac{7}{8}$ **52.** $(4, 2),$ slope $-\dfrac{1}{5}$

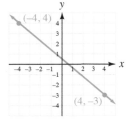   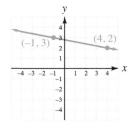

Use either the slope–intercept form (from Section 5.6) or the point–slope form (from Section 5.7) to find an equation of each line. Write each result in slope–intercept form, if possible.

53. Passes through $(5, 0)$ and $(-11, -4)$

54. Passes through $(7, -3)$ and $(-5, 1)$

55. Horizontal, passes through $(-8, 12)$

56. Horizontal, passes through $(9, -32)$

57. Slope $-\dfrac{1}{4}$, y-intercept $\left(0, \dfrac{7}{8}\right)$

58. Slope $-\dfrac{9}{5}$, y-intercept $\left(0, \dfrac{11}{3}\right)$

59. Slope $-\dfrac{2}{3}$, passes through $(3, 0)$

60. Slope $-\dfrac{2}{5}$, passes through $(15, 0)$

61. Slope 8, passes through $(2, 20)$

62. Slope 6, passes through $(1, -2)$

63. Vertical, passes through $(-3, 7)$

64. Vertical, passes through $(12, -23)$

65. Slope 7 and y-intercept $(0, -11)$

66. Slope 3 and y-intercept $(0, 4)$

67. Passes through $(-2, -1)$ and $(-1, -5)$

68. Passes through $(-3, 6)$ and $(-1, -4)$

69. x-intercept $(7, 0)$ and y-intercept $(0, -2)$

70. x-intercept $(-3, 0)$ and y-intercept $(0, 7)$

71. Slope $\dfrac{1}{10}$, passes through the origin

72. Slope $\dfrac{9}{8}$, passes through the origin

73. Undefined slope, passes through $\left(-\dfrac{1}{8}, 12\right)$

74. Undefined slope, passes through $\left(\dfrac{2}{5}, -\dfrac{5}{6}\right)$

75. Slope 1.7, y-intercept $(0, -2.8)$

76. Slope 9.5, y-intercept $(0, -14.3)$

77. ANATOMY There is a linear relationship between a woman's height and the length of her radius bone. It can be stated this way: Height increases by 3.9 inches for each 1-inch increase in the length of the radius. Suppose a 64-inch-tall woman has a 9-inch-long radius bone. Use this information to find a linear equation that relates height h to the length r of the radius. Write the equation in slope–intercept form.

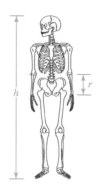

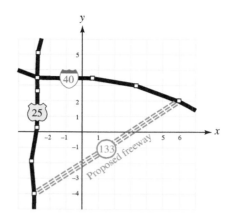

78. AUTOMATION An automated production line uses distilled water at a rate of 300 gallons every 2 hours to make shampoo. After the line had run for 7 hours, planners noted that 2,500 gallons of distilled water remained in the storage tank. Find a linear equation relating the time t in hours since the production line began and the number g of gallons of distilled water in the storage tank. Write the equation in slope–intercept form.

79. POLE VAULTING Find the equations of the lines that describe the positions of the pole for parts 1, 3, and 4 of the jump. Write the equations in slope–intercept form, if possible.

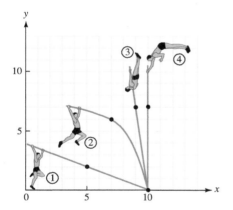

80. FREEWAY DESIGN The graph in the next column shows the route of a proposed freeway.

a. Give the coordinates of the points where the proposed Freeway 133 will join Interstate 25 and Highway 40.

b. Find an equation of the line that describes the route of the proposed freeway. Write the equation in slope–intercept form.

81. TOXIC CLEANUP Three months after cleanup began at a dump site, 800 cubic yards of toxic waste had yet to be removed. Two months later, that number had been lowered to 720 cubic yards.

a. Find an equation that describes the linear relationship between the length of time m (in months) the cleanup crew has been working and the number of cubic yards y of toxic waste remaining. Write the equation in slope–intercept form.

b. Use your answer to part (a) to predict the number of cubic yards of waste that will still be on the site one year after the cleanup project began.

82. DEPRECIATION To lower its corporate income tax, accountants of a company depreciated a word processing system over several years using a linear model, as shown in the worksheet.

a. Find a linear equation relating the years since the system was purchased, x, and its value, y, in dollars. Write the equation in slope–intercept form.

b. Find the purchase price of the system.

Tax Worksheet Method of depreciation: *Linear*

Property	Years after purchase	Value
Word processing system	2	$60,000
	4	$30,000

83. TRAMPOLINES There is a linear relationship between the length of the protective pad that wraps around a trampoline and the radius of the trampoline. Use the data in the table to find an equation that gives the length l of pad needed for any trampoline with radius r. Write the equation in slope–intercept form. Use units of feet for both l and r.

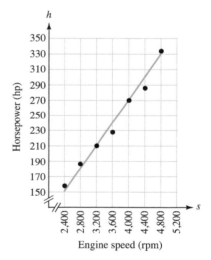

Radius	Pad length
3 ft	19 ft
7 ft	44 ft

84. RAISING A FAMILY In the report *"Expenditures on Children by Families,"* the U.S. Department of Agriculture projected the yearly child-rearing expenditures on children from birth through age 17. For a child born in 2010 to a two-parent middle-income family, the report estimated annual expenditures of $10,808 when the child is 6 years old, and $14,570 when the child is 15 years old.

  a. Write two ordered pairs of the form (child's age, annual expenditure).

  b. Assume the relationship between the child's age a and the annual expenditures E is linear. Use your answers to part (a) to write an equation in slope–intercept form that models this relationship.

  c. What are the projected child-rearing expenses when the child is 17 years old?

85. GOT MILK? The scatter diagram shows the amount of milk that an average American drank in one year for the years 1980–2008. A straight line can be used to model the data.

  a. Use the two highlighted points on the line to find its equation. Write the equation in slope–intercept form.

  b. Use your answer to part (a) to predict the amount of milk that an average American will drink in 2020.

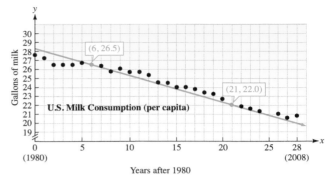

Source: United States Department of Agriculture.

86. ENGINE OUTPUT The horsepower produced by an automobile engine was recorded for various engine speeds in the range of 2,400 to 4,800 revolutions per minute (rpm). The data were recorded on the following scatter diagram. Find an equation of the line that models the relationship between engine speed s and horsepower h. Write the equation in slope–intercept form.

Engine speed (rpm)

WRITING

87. Why is $y - y_1 = m(x - x_1)$ called the point–slope form of the equation of a line?

88. If we know two points that a line passes through, we can write its equation. Explain how this is done.

89. Explain the steps involved in writing $y - 6 = 4(x - 1)$ in slope–intercept form.

90. Think of the points on the graph of the horizontal line $y = 4$. What do the points have in common? How do they differ?

SECTION 5.8
Applications Introduction Functions

The concept of a *function* is one of the most important ideas in all of mathematics. To introduce this topic, we will begin with a table that might be seen on television or printed in a newspaper. It shows the number of women serving in the U.S. House of Representatives for several recent sessions of Congress.

Women in the U.S. House of Representatives							
Session of Congress	105th	106th	107th	108th	109th	110th	111th
Number of Women Representatives	54	56	59	59	68	71	78

Source: womenincongress.house.gov

1. We can display the data in the table as a set of ordered pairs, where the **first component** represents the session of Congress and the **second component** represents the number of women representatives serving during that session. Fill in the missing first or second component.

    { (105,   ), (106,   ), (, 59), (108,   ), (, 68), (110,   ), (, 78) }

    Sets of ordered pairs like the one above are called **relations.** The set of all first components is called the **domain of the relation,** and the set of all second components is called the **range of the relation.** A relation may consist of a finite (countable) number of ordered pairs or an infinite (unlimited) number of ordered pairs.

3. Complete the domain and range of the House of Representatives relation. If a first or second component appears more than once, it need only be listed once when stating the domain or range.

    Domain: {105,   ,   ,   ,   ,   }
      Range: {54,   ,   ,   ,   }

    The House of Representatives relation was defined by a set of ordered pairs. Relations also can be defined using an **arrow** or **mapping diagram.**

3. Fill in the missing numbers in the following arrow diagram for the House of Representatives example.

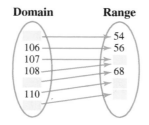

Domain   **Range**
106 → 54
107 → 56
108
110 → 68

Notice that to each session of Congress, there corresponds exactly one number of women representatives. That is, to each member of the domain, there corresponds exactly one member of the range. Relations that have this characteristic are called *functions*.

Function, Domain, Range

A **function** is a set of ordered pairs (a relation) in which to each first component there corresponds exactly one second component. The set of first components is called the **domain of the function,** and the set of second components is called the **range of the function.**

By this definition, the House of Representatives relation is a function. However, not all relations are functions, as you will see in the next problem.

4. THE WEATHER The monthly average high temperatures (in degrees Fahrenheit) for Pinehurst, North Carolina are shown as a relation below.

{ (50, Jan), (54, Feb), (62, Mar), (72, Apr), (79, May), (86, Jun), (89, Jul), (87, Aug), (82, Sep), (72, Oct), (63, Nov), (53, Dec) }

a. What two ordered pairs in the relation have the same first component but different second components?

b. Use your answer to part (a) to fill in the blanks: To the first component, 72, there corresponds two different second components, ____ and ____. For this reason, the relation is *not* a function.

c. Complete the arrow diagram for the given relation.

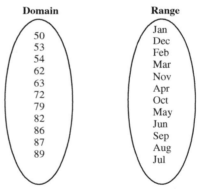

5. TOP TEN ALL-TIME DRIVERS The following relation shows the total number of career victories in NASCAR Cup Series competition, as of June 2012. Is this relation a function? Explain why or why not. (Source: gordononline.com)

{ (200, R. Petty), (105, Pearson), (85, Gordon), (84, Allison), (84, Waltrip), (83, Yarborough), (76, Earnhardt), (57, J. Johnson), (55, Wallace), (54, L. Petty) }

6. SHARK ATTACKS The table on the next page shows the number of shark attacks off the coast of Florida for the years 2000 through 2011.

a. Present the data in the table as a relation using ordered pairs of the form (year, total attacks).

b. In part a, is the relation that you wrote a function?

c. If the data in the table is presented as a relation using ordered pairs of the form (total attacks, year), is that relation a function? Explain why or why not.

YEAR	Total Attacks
2000	37
2001	34
2002	29
2003	29
2004	12
2005	17
2006	21
2007	31
2008	28
2009	19
2010	14
2011	11

(Source: Florida Museum of Natural History)

7. THE NFL Complete the arrow diagram below by matching the states with the proper National Football league teams. Does the diagram define a function? Explain why or why not.

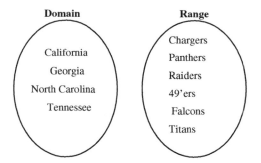

8. TEACHING ASSIGNMENTS The mathematics modules taught by several instructors are shown in the table below. If the information in the table is presented as a relation using ordered pairs of the form (instructor, module), is the relation a function? Explain why or why not.

Instructor name	Modules taught
Brown	DMA 030
Keller	DMA 050
McInerney	DMA 060
Paxon	DMA 070
Tucker	DMA 010, DMA 020
Willis	DMA 040

Objectives

1 Find the domain and range of a relation.

2 Identify functions and their domains and ranges.

3 Use function notation.

4 Graph functions.

5 Use the vertical line test.

6 Solve applications involving functions.

SECTION 5.8

An Introduction to Functions

ARE YOU READY?

The following problems review some basic skills that are needed when working with functions.

1. If $y = 3x - 1$, find the value for y when $x = 6$.

2. Which of the following ordered pairs have the same x-coordinate? $(3, 5)$, $(2, 9)$, $(3, 0)$, $(-1, 5)$

3. Which of the following ordered pairs have the same y-coordinate? $(8, 4)$, $(-7, 6)$, $(0, 0)$, $(-3, 4)$

4. Find each absolute value:

    a. $|-5|$ **b.** $|2|$

In this section, we will discuss *relations* and *functions*. These two concepts are included in our study of graphing because they involve ordered pairs.

1 Find the domain and range of a relation.

The following table shows the number of medals won by American athletes at several recent Winter Olympics.

USA Winter Olympic Medal Count

Year	1988	1992	1994*	1998	2002	2006	2010
Medals	6	11	13	13	34	25	37
	Calgary CAN	Albertville FRA	Lillehammer NOR	Nagano JPN	Salt Lake City USA	Turin ITA	Vancouver CAN

* The Winter Olympics were moved ahead two years so that the winter and summer games would alternate every two years.

We can display the data in the table as a set of ordered pairs, where the **first component** represents the year and the **second component** represents the number of medals won by American athletes:

$$\{(1988, 6), (1992, 11), (1994, 13), (1998, 13), (2002, 34), (2006, 25), (2010, 37)\}$$

A set of ordered pairs, such as this, is called a **relation.** The set of all first components is called the **domain** of the relation and the set of all second components is called the **range** of the relation.

Self Check 1

Find the domain and range of the relation $\{(8, 2), (-1, 10), (6, 2), (-5, -5)\}$.

Now Try Problem 15

EXAMPLE 1   Find the domain and range of the relation $\{(1, 7), (4, -6), (-3, 1), (2, 7)\}$.

Strategy We will examine the first and second components of the ordered pairs.

WHY The set of first components is the domain and the set of second components is the range.

Solution

The relation $\{(1, 7), (4, -6), (-3, 1), (2, 7)\}$ has the domain $\{-3, 1, 2, 4\}$ and the range is $\{-6, 1, 7\}$. The elements of the domain and range are usually listed in increasing order, and if a value is repeated, it is listed only once.

2 Identify functions and their domains and ranges.

An **arrow** or **mapping diagram** can be used to define a relation. The data from the Winter Olympics example are shown on the right in that form. Relations are also often defined using **two-column tables**.

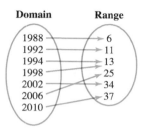

Notice that for each year, there corresponds exactly one medal count. That is, this relation assigns to each member of the domain exactly one member of the range. Relations that have this characteristic are called *functions*.

Function

A **function** is a set of ordered pairs (a relation) in which to each first component there corresponds exactly one second component.

We may also think of a function as a rule that assigns to each value of one variable exactly one value of another variable. Since we often worked with sets of ordered pairs of the form (x, y), it is helpful to define a function in an alternate way using the variables x and y.

---

y Is a Function of *x*

Given a relation in x and y, if to each value of x in the domain there is assigned exactly one value of y in the range, then y is said to be a function of x.

EXAMPLE 2   Determine whether each relation defines y to be a function of x. If a function is defined, give its domain and range.

a.
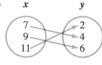

b.

x	y
2	3
5	7
2	1
6	5

c. $\{(0, 8), (3, 8), (4, 8), (9, 8)\}$

d.

Strategy We will check to see whether each value of x is assigned exactly one value of y.

WHY If this is true, then y is a function of x.

Solution

a. The arrow diagram defines a function because to each value of x there is assigned exactly one value of y: $7 \to 4$, $9 \to 6$, and $11 \to 2$.

   The domain of the function is $\{7, 9, 11\}$ and the range is $\{2, 4, 6\}$.

b. The table does not define a function, because to the x value 2 there is assigned more than one value of y: $2 \to 3$ and $2 \to 1$.

Self Check 2

Determine whether each relation defines y to be a function of x. If a function is defined, give its domain and range.

a.
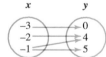

b.

x	y
-6	-6
5	5
4	8

c. $\{(1, 4), (4, 9), (9, 4), (3, 9)\}$

Now Try Problems 19, 25, and 31

c. Since to each number x exactly one value y is assigned, the set of ordered pairs defines y to be a function of x. It also illustrates an important fact about functions: *The same value of y can be assigned to different values of x.* In this case, each number x is assigned the y-value 8.

The domain of the function is $\{0, 3, 4, 9\}$ and the range is $\{8\}$.

d. The arrow diagram does not define a function, because to the x value -4 there is assigned more than one value of y: $-4 \rightarrow 6$ and $-4 \rightarrow 11$.

3 Use function notation.

12	4
13	6
14	12
15	9

A function can be defined by an equation. For example, $y = 2x - 3$ is a rule that assigns to each value of x exactly one value of y. To find the y-value that is assigned to the x-value 4, we substitute 4 for x and evaluate the right side of the equation.

$$y = 2x - 3$$
$$y = 2(4) - 3 \quad \text{Substitute 4 for } x.$$
$$= 8 - 3 \quad \text{Evaluate the right side.}$$
$$= 5$$

The function $y = 2x - 3$ assigns the y-value 5 to an x-value of 4. When making such calculations, the value of x is called an **input** and its corresponding value of y is called an **output.**

A special notation is used to name functions that are defined by equations.

Function Notation

The notation $y = f(x)$ indicates that the variable y is a function of x.

If y is a function of x, then y and $f(x)$ are interchangeable. The symbol $f(x)$ does not mean $f \cdot x$. We read $f(x)$ as "f of x" or as "the value of f at x."

Since $y = f(x)$, the equations $y = 2x - 3$ and $f(x) = 2x - 3$ are equivalent. We read $f(x) = 2x - 3$ as "f of x is equal to $2x$ minus 3."

This is the variable used to represent the input value.
$$\downarrow$$
$$f(x) = 2x - 3$$
$$\uparrow \qquad\qquad \uparrow$$
This is the name of the function.   This expression shows how to obtain an output from a given input.

Function notation provides a compact way of representing the value that is assigned to some number x. For example, if $f(x) = 2x - 3$, the value that is assigned to an x-value 5 is represented by $f(5)$.

$$f(x) = 2x - 3$$
$$f(5) = 2(5) - 3 \quad \text{Substitute the input 5 for each } x.$$
$$= 10 - 3 \quad \text{Evaluate the right side.}$$
$$= 7 \quad \text{The output is 7.}$$

Thus, $f(5) = 7$. We read this as "f of 5 is 7." The output 7 is called a **function value.**

To see why function notation is helpful, consider these two sentences, which ask you to do the same thing:

1. If $y = 2x - 3$, find the value of y when x is 5.

2. If $f(x) = 2x - 3$, find $f(5)$.

Sentence 2, which uses $f(x)$ notation, is much more compact.

EXAMPLE 3   For $f(x) = 5x + 7$, find each of the following function values:
a. $f(2)$ **b.** $f(-4)$ **c.** $f(0)$

Strategy We will substitute 2, −4, and 0 for x in the expression $5x + 7$ and then evaluate it.

WHY The notation $f(x) = 5x + 7$ indicates that we are to multiply each input (each number written within the parentheses) by 5 and then add 7 to that product.

Solution

a. To find $f(2)$, we substitute the number within the parentheses, 2, for each x in $f(x) = 5x + 7$, and evaluate the right side of the equation.

$f(x) = 5x + 7$
$f(2) = 5(2) + 7$ Substitute the input 2 for each x.
$\quad\ = 10 + 7$ Evaluate the right side.
$\quad\ = 17$ The output is 17.

Thus, $f(2) = 17$.   Another way to read $f(2) = 17$ is to say "the value of f at 2 is 17."

b. $f(x) = 5x + 7$
$f(-4) = 5(-4) + 7$ Substitute the input −4 for each x.
$\quad\ = -20 + 7$ Evaluate the right side.
$\quad\ = -13$ The output is −13.

Thus, $f(-4) = -13$.

c. $f(x) = 5x + 7$
$f(0) = 5(0) + 7$ Substitute the input 0 for each x.
$\quad\ = 0 + 7$ Evaluate the right side.
$\quad\ = 7$ The output is 7.

Thus, $f(0) = 7$.

We can think of a function as a machine that takes some input x and turns it into some output $f(x)$, as shown in part (a) of the figure below. In part (b), the function machine for $f(x) = x^2 + 2x$ turns the input 4 into the output $4^2 + 2(4) = 24$, and we have $f(4) = 24$.

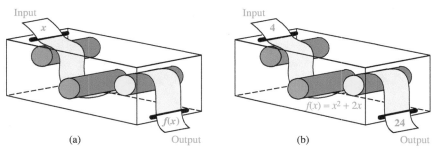

(a)   Output   (b)   Output

The letter f used in the notation $y = f(x)$ represents the word *function*. However, other letters, such as g and h, can also be used to name functions.

EXAMPLE 4   For $g(x) = 3 - 2x$ and $h(x) = x^3 + x^2 - 1$, find: **a.** $g(3)$
b. $h(-2)$

Strategy We will substitute 3 for x in $3 - 2x$ and substitute −2 for x in $x^3 + x^2 - 1$, and then evaluate each expression.

Self Check 3

For $f(x) = -2x + 3$, find each of the following function values:

a. $f(4)$
b. $f(-1)$
c. $f(0)$

Now Try Problem 35

Self Check 4

Find $g(0)$ and $h(4)$ for the functions in Example 4.

Now Try **Problem 41**

WHY The numbers 3 and -2, which are within the parentheses, are inputs that should be substituted for the variable x.

Solution

a. To find $g(3)$, we use the function rule $g(x) = 3 - 2x$ and replace x with 3.

$$g(x) = 3 - 2x \qquad \text{Read } g(x) \text{ as "g of x."}$$
$$g(3) = 3 - 2(3) \qquad \text{Substitute the input 3 for each x.}$$
$$= 3 - 6 \qquad \text{Evaluate the right side.}$$
$$= -3 \qquad \text{The output is } -3.$$

Thus, $g(3) = -3$.

b. To find $h(-2)$, we use the function rule $h(x) = x^3 + x^2 - 1$ and replace x with -2.

$$h(x) = x^3 + x^2 - 1 \qquad \text{Read } h(x) \text{ as "h of x."}$$
$$h(-2) = (-2)^3 + (-2)^2 - 1 \qquad \text{Substitute the input } -2 \text{ for each x.}$$
$$= -8 + 4 - 1 \qquad \text{Evaluate the right side.}$$
$$= -5 \qquad \text{This is the output.}$$

Thus, $h(-2) = -5$.

4 Graph functions.

We have seen that a function such as $f(x) = 4x + 1$ assigns to each value of x a single value $f(x)$. The input-output pairs generated by a function can be written in the form $(x, f(x))$. These ordered pairs can be plotted on a rectangular coordinate system to give the **graph of the function.**

Self Check 5

Graph: $f(x) = -3x - 2$

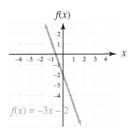

Now Try **Problem 47**

EXAMPLE 5   Graph: $f(x) = 4x + 1$

Strategy We can graph the function by creating a table of function values and plotting the corresponding ordered pairs.

WHY After drawing a line through the plotted points, we will have the graph of the function.

Solution

To make a table, we choose several values for x and find the corresponding values of $f(x)$. If x is -1, we have

$$f(x) = 4x + 1 \qquad \text{This is the function to graph.}$$
$$f(-1) = 4(-1) + 1 \qquad \text{Substitute the input } -1 \text{ for each x.}$$
$$= -4 + 1 \qquad \text{Evaluate the right side.}$$
$$= -3 \qquad \text{This is the output.}$$

Thus, $f(-1) = -3$. This means when x is -1, $f(x)$ or y is -3, and that the ordered pair $(-1, -3)$ lies on the graph of $f(x)$.

Function notation	*Ordered-pair notation*
$f(-1) = -3$	$(-1, -3)$

Similarly, we find the corresponding values of $f(x)$ for x-values of 0 and 1. Then we plot the resulting ordered pairs and draw a straight line through them to get the graph of $f(x) = 4x + 1$. Since $y = f(x)$, the graph of $f(x) = 4x + 1$ is the same as the graph of the equation $y = 4x + 1$.

A table of function values is similar to a table of solutions, except that the second column is usually labeled f(x) instead of y.

$f(x) = 4x + 1$

x	f(x)
−1	−3
0	1
1	5

−1 −3 → (−1, −3)
0 1 → (0, 1)
1 5 → (1, 5)

The function generates these ordered pairs.

The vertical axis can be labeled y or f(x).

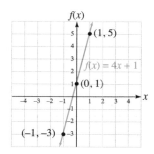

We call $f(x) = 4x + 1$ from Example 5 a **linear function** because its graph is a nonvertical line. Any linear equation, except those of the form $x = a$, can be written using function notation by writing it in slope–intercept form ($y = mx + b$) and then replacing y with $f(x)$.

The graphs of some functions are not straight lines.

EXAMPLE 6   Graph: $f(x) = |x|$

Strategy We can graph the function by creating a table of function values and plotting the corresponding ordered pairs.

WHY After drawing a "V" shape through the plotted points, we will have the graph of the function.

Solution
To create a table of function values, we choose values for x and find the corresponding values of $f(x)$. For $x = -4$ and $x = 3$, we have

$$f(x) = |x| \qquad f(x) = |x|$$
$$f(-4) = |-4| \qquad f(3) = |3|$$
$$= 4 \qquad\qquad = 3$$

The results $f(-4) = 4$ and $f(3) = 3$ produce the ordered pairs $(-4, 4)$ and $(3, 3)$.

Similarly, we find the corresponding values of $f(x)$ for several other x-values. When we plot the resulting ordered pairs, we see that they lie in a "V" shape. We join the points to complete the graph as shown. We call $f(x) = |x|$ an **absolute value function**.

$f(x) = |x|$

x	f(x)
−4	4
−3	3
−2	2
−1	1
0	0
1	1
2	2
3	3
4	4

−4 4 → (−4, 4)
−3 3 → (−3, 3)
−2 2 → (−2, 2)
−1 1 → (−1, 1)
0 0 → (0, 0)
1 1 → (1, 1)
2 2 → (2, 2)
3 3 → (3, 3)
4 4 → (4, 4)

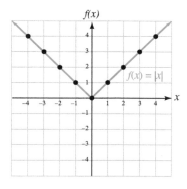

Self Check 6

Graph: $f(x) = |x| + 2$

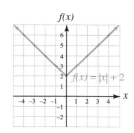

Now Try **Problem 49**

5   Use the vertical line test.

If any vertical line intersects a graph more than once, the graph cannot represent a function, because to one value of *x* there would correspond more than one value of *y*.

The Vertical Line Test

If a vertical line intersects a graph in more than one point, the graph is not the graph of a function.

The graph shown on the right in red does not represent a function, because a vertical line intersects the graph at more than one point. The points of intersection indicate that the *x*-value −1 corresponds to two different *y*-values, 3 and −1.

When the coordinates of the two points of intersection are listed in a table, it is easy to see that the *x*-value of −1 is assigned two different *y*-values. Thus, this is not the graph of a function.

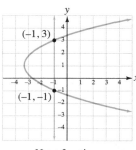

Not a function

x	*y*
−1	3
−1	−1

Now Try Problems 55 and 57

Self Check 7

Determine whether each of the following is the graph of a function.

a.

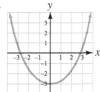

b.

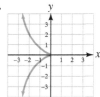

EXAMPLE 7   Determine whether each of the graphs shown in red is the graph of a function.

a.

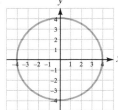

b.

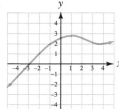

c.

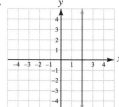

Strategy We will check to see whether any vertical line intersects the graph more than once.

WHY If any vertical line does intersect the graph more than once, the graph is not a function.

Solution

a. Refer to figure (a) on the next page. The graph shown in red is not the graph of a function, because a vertical line can be drawn that intersects the graph at more than one point. The points of intersection of the graph and the line reveal that the *x*-value 3 is assigned two different *y*-values, 2.5 and −2.5.

b. Refer to figure (b) on the next page. The graph shown in red is a graph of a function, because no vertical line can be drawn that intersects the graph at more than one point. Several vertical lines are drawn in blue to illustrate this.

c. Refer to figure (c) on the next page. The graph shown in red is not the graph of a function, because a vertical line can be drawn that intersects the graph at more than one point. In fact, it intersects it at infinitely many points. From this example, we can conclude that any vertical line will fail the vertical line test. Thus, vertical lines are not functions.

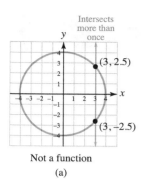

Intersects more than once

Not a function
(a)

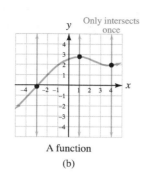

Only intersects once

A function
(b)

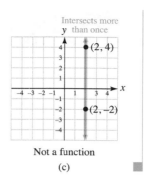

Intersects more than once

Not a function
(c)

6 Solve applications involving functions.

Functions are used to describe certain relationships where one quantity depends on another. Letters other than f and x are often chosen to more clearly describe these situations.

EXAMPLE 8 *Bounce Houses* The function $C(h) = 80 + 15(h - 4)$ gives the cost in dollars to rent an inflatable jumper for h hours. (The terms of the rental agreement require a 4-hour minimum.) Find the cost of renting the jumper for 10 hours.

Strategy To find the cost to rent the jumper for 10 hours, we will substitute 10 for each h in $C(h) = 80 + 15(h - 4)$ and evaluate the right side.

WHY In $C(h) = 80 + 15(h - 4)$, the variable h represents the number of hours that the jumper is rented. We need to find $C(10)$.

Solution
For this application involving hours and cost, the notation $C(h)$ is used. The input variable is h and the name of the function is C. If the jumper is rented for 10 hours, then h is 10 and we must find $C(10)$.

$$C(h) = 80 + 15(h - 4) \qquad \text{Read } C(h) \text{ as "C of h."}$$
$$C(10) = 80 + 15(10 - 4) \qquad \text{Substitute the input 10 for each } h.$$
$$= 80 + 15(6) \qquad \text{Evaluate the right side.}$$
$$= 80 + 90 \qquad \text{Do the multiplication.}$$
$$= 170 \qquad \text{This is the output.}$$

It costs $170 to rent the jumper for 10 hours.

Self Check 8

BOUNCE HOUSES Find the cost of renting the jumper for 8 hours.

Now Try **Problem 65**

©iStockphoto.com/TIM MCCAIG

ANSWERS TO SELF CHECKS

1. Domain: $\{-5, -1, 6, 8\}$; Range: $\{-5, 2, 10\}$ **2. a.** Not a function: $-1 \rightarrow 4$ and $-1 \rightarrow 5$
b. Function: domain: $\{-6, 4, 5\}$; range $\{-6, 5, 8\}$ **c.** Function: domain: $\{1, 3, 4, 9\}$; range $\{4, 9\}$
3. a. -5 **b.** 5 **c.** 3 **4.** $3, 79$ **5.**

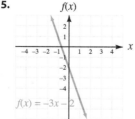

6.

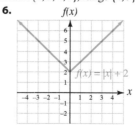

7. a. Function **b.** Not a function

SECTION 5.8   STUDY SET

VOCABULARY

Fill in the blanks.

1. A set of ordered pairs is called a _____.
2. A _____ is a rule that assigns to each *x*-value exactly one *y*-value.
3. The set of all input values for a function is called the _____, and the set of all output values is called the _____.
4. We can think of a function as a machine that takes some _____ *x* and turns it into some output ____.
5. If $f(2) = -3$, we call -3 a function _____.
6. The graph of a _____ function is a straight line and the graph of an _____ value function is V-shaped.

CONCEPTS

7. FEDERAL MINIMUM HOURLY WAGE The following table is an example of a function. Use an arrow diagram to illustrate this.

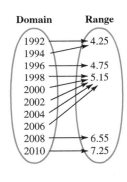

Year	Minimum wage ($)
1992	4.25
1994	4.25
1996	4.75
1998	5.15
2000	5.15
2002	5.15
2004	5.15
2006	5.15
2008	6.55
2010	7.25

Source: infoplease.com

8. The arrow diagram describes a function. What is the domain and what is the range of the function?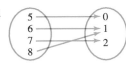

9. For the given input, what value will the function machine output?

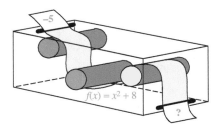

10. **a.** Fill in the blank: If a _____ line intersects a graph in more than one point, the graph is not the graph of a function.

    b. Give the coordinates of the points where the given vertical line intersects the graph.

    c. Is this the graph of a function?

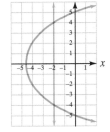

NOTATION

Fill in the blanks.

11. We read $f(x) = 5x - 6$ as "*f* ___ *x* is 5*x* minus 6."
12. Since $y =$ ____, the following two equations are equivalent:
    $$y = 3x + 2 \text{ and } f(x) = 3x + 2$$
13. The notation $f(4) = 5$ indicates that when the *x*-value ▢ is input into a function rule, the output is ▢. This fact can be shown graphically by plotting the ordered pair (▢ , ▢).
14. When graphing the function $f(x) = -x + 5$, the vertical axis of the coordinate system can be labeled ▢ or ▢.

GUIDED PRACTICE

Find the domain and range of each relation. **See Example 1.**

15. $\{(6, -1), (-1, -10), (-6, 2), (8, -5)\}$

16. $\{(11, -3), (0, 0), (4, 5), (-3, -7)\}$

17. $\{(0, 9), (-8, 50), (6, 9)\}$

18. $\{(1, -12), (-6, 8), (5, 8)\}$

Determine whether the relation defines y to be a function of x. If a function is defined, give its domain and range. If it does not define a function, find two ordered pairs that show a value of x that is assigned more than one value of y. See Example 2.

19.

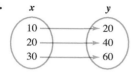

20.

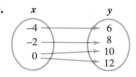

21.

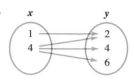

22.

x   y

5
10 → 15
15

23.

x	y
1	7
2	15
3	23
4	16
5	8

24.

x	y
30	2
30	4
30	6
30	8
30	10

25.

x	y
−4	6
−1	0
0	−3
2	4
−1	2

26.

x	y
1	1
2	2
3	3
4	4

27.

x	y
3	4
3	−4
4	3
4	−3

28.

x	y
−1	1
−3	1
−5	1
−7	1
−9	1

29.

x	y
6	0
−3	−8
1	9
5	4

30.

x	y
1.6	0
−3	−1
2.5	20
−7	0.1
1.6	19

31. $\{(3, 4), (3, -4), (4, 3), (4, -3)\}$

32. $\{(-1, 1), (-3, 1), (-5, 1), (-7, 1), (-9, 1)\}$

33. $\{(-2, 7), (-1, 10), (0, 13), (1, 16)\}$

34. $\{(-2, 4), (-3, 8), (-3, 12), (-4, 16)\}$

Find each function value. See Examples 3 and 4.

35. $f(x) = 4x - 1$

     a. $f(1)$ **b.** $f(-2)$ **c.** $f\left(\dfrac{1}{4}\right)$ **d.** $f(50)$

36. $f(x) = 1 - 5x$

     a. $f(0)$ **b.** $f(-75)$ **c.** $f(0.2)$ **d.** $f\left(-\dfrac{4}{5}\right)$

37. $f(x) = 2x^2$

     a. $f(0.4)$ **b.** $f(-3)$ **c.** $f(1,000)$ **d.** $f\left(\dfrac{1}{8}\right)$

38. $g(x) = 6 - x^2$

     a. $g(30)$ **b.** $g(6)$ **c.** $g(-1)$ **d.** $g(0.5)$

39. $h(x) = |x - 7|$

     a. $h(0)$ **b.** $h(-7)$ **c.** $h(7)$ **d.** $h(8)$

40. $f(x) = |2 + x|$

     a. $f(0)$ **b.** $f(2)$ **c.** $f(-2)$ **d.** $f(-99)$

41. $g(x) = x^3 - x$

     a. $g(1)$ **b.** $g(10)$ **c.** $g(-3)$ **d.** $g(6)$

42. $g(x) = x^4 + x$

     a. $g(1)$ **b.** $g(-2)$ **c.** $g(0)$ **d.** $g(10)$

43. $s(x) = (x + 3)^2$

     a. $s(3)$ **b.** $s(-3)$ **c.** $s(0)$ **d.** $s(-5)$

44. $s(x) = (x - 8)^2$

     a. $s(8)$ **b.** $s(-8)$ **c.** $s(1)$ **d.** $s(12)$

45. If $f(x) = 3.4x^2 - 1.2x + 0.5$, find $f(-0.3)$.

46. If $g(x) = x^4 - x^3 + x^2 - x$, find $g(-12)$.

Complete each table of function values and then graph each function. See Examples 5 and 6.

47. $f(x) = -3x - 2$

x	f(x)
-2	
-1	
0	
1	

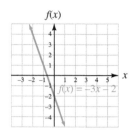

48. $f(x) = -2x + 8$

x	f(x)
-1	
0	
1	
2	

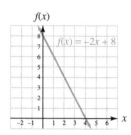

49. $h(x) = |1 - x|$

x	h(x)
-2	
-1	
0	
1	
2	
3	
4	

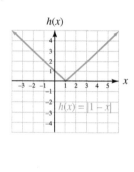

50. $h(x) = |x + 2|$

x	h(x)
-5	
-4	
-3	
-2	
-1	
0	
1	

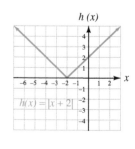

Graph each function. See Examples 5 and 6.

51. $f(x) = \frac{1}{2}x - 2$

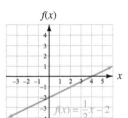

52. $f(x) = -\frac{2}{3}x + 3$

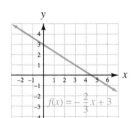

53. $h(x) = |-x|$

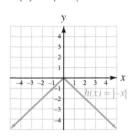

54. $g(x) = |x| - 2$

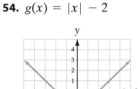

Determine whether each graph is the graph of a function. If it is not, find ordered pairs that show a value of x that is assigned more than one value of y. See Example 7.

55.

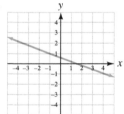

56.

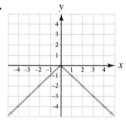

57.

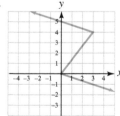

58.

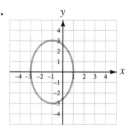

59.
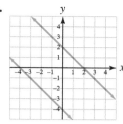

60.
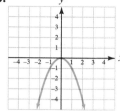

61.
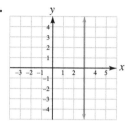

62.
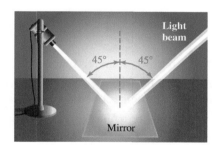

(3 day minimum)

66. STRUCTURAL ENGINEERING The maximum safe load in pounds of the rectangular beam shown in the figure is given by the function $S(t) = \dfrac{1,875t^2}{8}$, where t is the thickness of the beam, in inches. Find the maximum safe load if the beam is 4 inches thick.

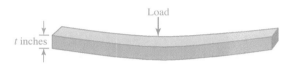

APPLICATIONS

63. REFLECTIONS When a beam of light hits a mirror, it is reflected off the mirror at the same angle that the incoming beam struck the mirror. What type of function could serve as a mathematical model for the path of the light beam shown below?

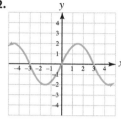

Light beam

45°   45°

Mirror

64. LIGHTNING The function $D(t) = \dfrac{t}{5}$ gives the approximate distance in miles that you are from a lightning strike, where t is the number of seconds between seeing the lightning and hearing the thunder. Find $D(5)$ and explain what it means.

65. VACATIONING The function $C(d) = 500 + 100(d - 3)$ gives the cost in dollars to rent an RV motor home for d days. (The terms of the rental agreement require a 3-day minimum.) Find the cost of renting the RV for a vacation that will last 7 days.

67. LAWN SPRINKLERS The function $A(r) = \pi r^2$ can be used to determine the area in square feet that will be watered by a rotating sprinkler that sprays out a stream of water. Find $A(5)$ and $A(20)$. Round to the nearest tenth.

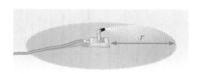

68. PARTS LISTS The function $f(r) = 2.30 + 3.25(r + 0.40)$ approximates the length (in feet) of the belt that joins the two pulleys, where r is the radius (in feet) of the smaller pulley. Find the belt length needed for each pulley in the parts list.

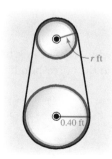

Parts list		
Pulley	r	**Belt length**
P-45M	0.32	
P-08D	0.24	

69. POSTAGE The **step graph** below shows how the cost of a first class U.S. postage stamp increased from 1990 through 2010. An open circle at the end of a line segment means the endpoint of the segment is not included. Is this the graph of a function?

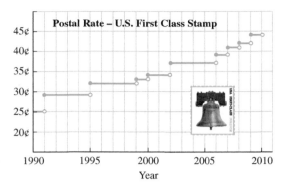

Source: U.S. Postal Service

70. SOUND We cannot see sound waves, but certain scientific instruments are used to draw mathematical models of them. Is the graph of a sound wave shown below a function?

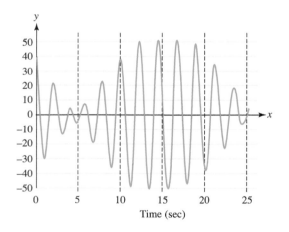

WRITING

71. In the function $y = -5x + 2$, why do you think the value of x is called the *input* and the corresponding value of y the *output*?

72. Explain what a politician meant when she said, "The speed at which the downtown area will be redeveloped is a function of the number of low-interest loans made available to the property owners."

73. Explain the following diagram:

$$f(4) = 11 \qquad\qquad (4, 11)$$

74. Explain the error in the following solution.

If $f(x) = x^2 + 7x + 1$, find $f(10)$.

$$f(10) = 10^2 + 7x + 1$$
$$= 100 + 7x + 1$$
$$= 101 + 7x$$

75. A student was asked to determine whether the graph on the right is the graph of a function. What is wrong with the following reasoning?

When I draw a vertical line through the graph, it intersects the graph only once. By the vertical line test, this is the graph of a function.

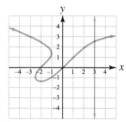

76. In your own words, what is a function?

77. Given the function $f(x) = -3x + 7$, describe the meaning of $f(2)$ using full sentences.

78. a. Is it possible for a function to have more numbers in the domain than the range? Explain why or why not.

b. Is it possible for a function to have more numbers in the range than in the domain? Explain why or why not.

MODULE 5 TEST

1. Fill in the blanks.

   a. A rectangular coordinate system is formed by two perpendicular number lines called the x-_____ and the y-_____.

   b. A _____ of an equation in two variables is an ordered pair of numbers that makes the equation a true statement.

   c. $3x + y = 10$ is a _____ equation in two variables and its graph is a line.

   d. The _____ of a line is a measure of steepness.

   e. $y - y_1 = m(x - x_1)$ is called the _____ form of the equation of a line. In words, we read this as y minus y _____ one equals m _____ the quantity of x _____ x sub _____.

   f. $y = mx + b$ is called the _____ form of the equation of a line.

   g. A _____ is a set of ordered pairs in which to each first component there corresponds exactly one second component.

   h. The set of all input values for a function is called the _____, the set of all output values is called the _____.

   i. $f(x) = 6 - 5x$ is an example of _____ notation.

2. WORKOUTS Refer to the table below to answer the following questions.

Number of Calories Burned While Running for One Hour

Running speed (mph)	Body Weight		
	130 lb	155 lb	190 lb
5	472	563	690
6	590	704	863
7	679	809	992
8	797	950	1,165
9	885	1,056	1,294

Source: nutristrategy.com

   a. How many calories will a 155-pound person burn if she runs for one hour at a rate of 5 mph?

   b. In one hour, how many more calories will a 190-pound person burn if he runs at a rate of 7 mph instead of 6 mph?

   c. At what rate does a 130-pound person have to run for one hour to burn approximately 800 calories?

3. MOVING Refer to the bar graph below to answer the following questions.

   a. Which piece of furniture shown in the graph requires the greatest number of feet of bubble wrap? How much?

   b. How many more feet of bubble wrap is needed to wrap a desk than a coffee table?

   c. How many feet of bubble wrap is needed to cover a bedroom set that has a headboard, a dresser, and two end tables?

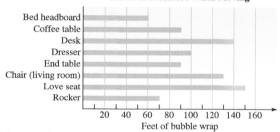

Amount of Bubble Wrap Needed to Wrap Pieces of Furniture When Moving

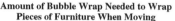

Source: transitsystems.com

4. CANCER SURVIVAL RATES Refer to the graph below to answer the following questions.

   a. What was the survival rate (in percent) from breast cancer in 1976?

   b. By how many percent did the cancer survival rate for breast cancer increase by 2008?

   c. Which type of cancer shown in the graph has the lowest survival rate?

   d. Which type of cancer has had the greatest increase in survival rate from 1976 to 2008? How much of an increase?

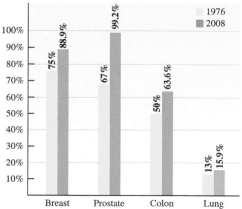

Five-Year Survival Rates

Source: SEER Cancer Statistics Review

5. ENERGY DRINKS Refer to the pictograph below to answer the following questions.

Sugar Content in Energy Drinks and Coffee
(12-ounce serving)

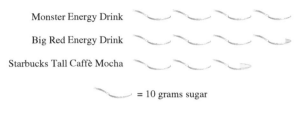

Monster Energy Drink

Big Red Energy Drink

Starbucks Tall Caffè Mocha

= 10 grams sugar

Source: energyfiend.com

a. How many grams of sugar are there in 12 ounces of Big Red?

b. For a 12-ounce serving, how many more grams of sugar are there in Monster Energy Drink than in Starbucks Tall Caffè Mocha?

6. FIRES Refer to the graph below to answer the following questions.

a. In 2010, what percent of the fires in the United States were vehicle fires?

b. In 2010, there were a total of 1,331,500 fires in the United States. How many were structure fires?

Where Fires Occurred, 2010

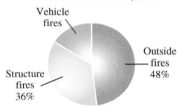

Vehicle fires

Outside fires
48%

Structure fires
36%

Source: U.S. Fire Administration

7. Refer to the line graph in the next column to answer the following questions.

a. How many eggs were produced in Nebraska in 2001?

b. How many eggs were produced in North Carolina in 2008?

c. In what year was the egg production of Nebraska equal to that of North Carolina? How many eggs?

d. What was the total egg production of Nebraska and North Carolina in 2005?

e. Between what two years did the egg production in North Carolina increase dramatically?

f. Between what two years did the egg production in Nebraska decrease dramatically?

g. How many more eggs did North Carolina produce in 2009 compared to Nebraska?

h. How many more eggs did Nebraska produce in 2000 compared to North Carolina?

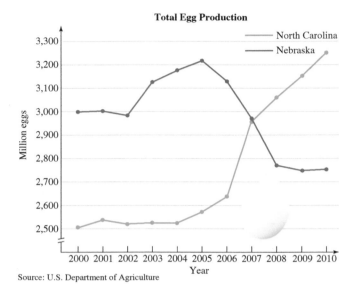

Total Egg Production

Source: U.S. Department of Agriculture

8. SKATEBOARDING Refer to the line graphs below that show the results of a skateboarding race.

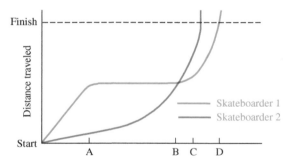

a. Which skateboarder had traveled farther at time A?

b. Describe what was happening between times A and C?

c. When were the skateboarders tied for the lead?

d. Did skateboarder 2 ever stop during the race? If so, when?

e. Which skateboarder won the race?

9. **COMMUTING TIME** A school district collected data on the number of minutes it took its employees to drive to work in the morning. The results are presented in the histogram below.

   a. How many employees have a commute time that is in the 7-to-10-minute range?

   b. How many employees have a commute time that is less than 10 minutes?

   c. How many employees have a commute that takes 15 minutes or more each day?

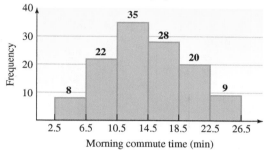

School District Employees' Commute

10. The graph shows the number of dogs being boarded in a kennel over a 3-day holiday weekend.

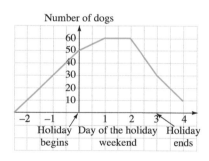

   a. How many dogs were in the kennel 2 days before the holiday?

   b. What is the maximum number of dogs that were boarded on the holiday weekend at any one time?

   c. When were there 30 dogs in the kennel?

   d. What information does the *y*-intercept of the graph give?

11. Plot each point on a rectangular coordinate system: $(1, 3)$, $(-2, 4)$, $(-3, -2)$, $(3, -2)$, $(21, 0)$, $(0, 21)$, and $\left(-\frac{1}{2}, \frac{7}{2}\right)$.

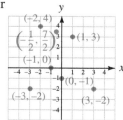

12. Find the coordinates of each point shown in the graph.

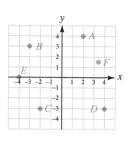

13. **HAWAII** Estimate the coordinates of Oahu using an ordered pair of the form (longitude, latitude).

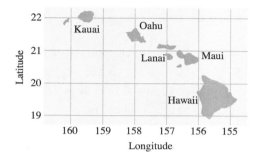

14. **GEOMETRY** Three vertices (corners) of a square are $(-5, 4)$, $(-5, -2)$, and $(1, -2)$. Find the coordinates of the fourth vertex and then find the area of the square.

15. **SNOWFALL** The graph below gives the amount of snow on the ground at a mountain resort as measured once each day over a 7-day period.

   a. On the first day, how much snow was on the ground?

   b. What was the difference in the amount of snow on the ground when the measurements were taken on the second and third day?

   c. How much snow was on the ground on the sixth day?

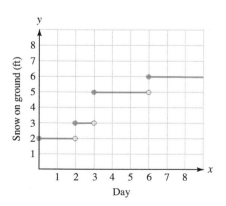

16. Use the graph in the illustration to complete the table.

x	y
3	
	0
−3	

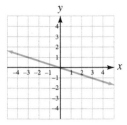

17. In what quadrant does the point $(-3, -4)$ lie?

18. In which quadrant is each point located?
   a. $(-1, -5)$ **b.** $\left(6, -2\frac{3}{4}\right)$

19. Is $(-3, -4)$ a solution of $3x - 4y = 7$?

20. Complete the table of solutions for the linear equation $x + 4y = 6$.

x	y	xy
2		
	3	

21. Determine whether $(-3, 5)$ is a solution of $y = |2 + x|$.

22. a. Complete the following table of solutions and graph the equation $y = -x^3$.

x	y	(x, y)
−2		
−1		
0		
1		
2		

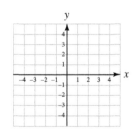

23. Graph: $y = x^2 - 4$ **24.** $y = |x - 2|$

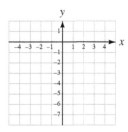   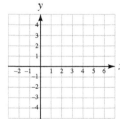

25. Graph: $y = 2x - 3$

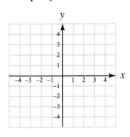

26. The graph shows the relationship between the number of oranges O an acre of land will yield if t orange trees are planted on it.
   a. If $t = 70$, what is O?
   b. What importance does the point $(40, 18)$ on the graph have?

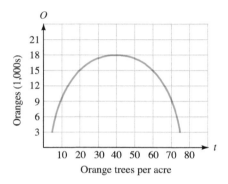

27. Which of the following equations are not linear equations?
$$8x - 2y = 6 \qquad y = x^2 + 1 \qquad y = x \qquad y - x^3 = 0$$

28. The graph of a linear equation is shown.
   a. When the coordinates of point A are substituted into the equation, will a true or false statement result?

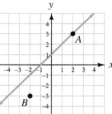

   b. When the coordinates of point B are substituted into the equation, will a true or false statement result?

29. Graph: $y = \dfrac{x}{3}$

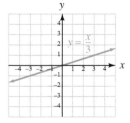

30. BIRTHDAY PARTIES A restaurant offers a party package for children that includes everything: food, drinks, cake, and favors. The cost c, in dollars, is given by the equation $c = 8n + 50$, where n is the number of children attending the party. Graph the equation and use the graph to estimate the cost of a party if 18 children attend.

31. Determine whether each statement is true or false.

   a. It takes three or more points to determine a line.

   b. A linear equation in two variables has infinitely many solutions.

32. Identify the x- and y-intercepts of the graph shown below.

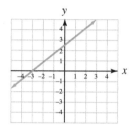

33. DEPRECIATION The graph below shows how the value of some sound equipment decreased over the years. Find the intercepts of the graph. What information do the intercepts give about the equipment?

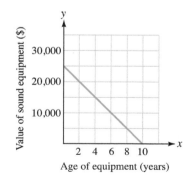

34. VALUE OF A CAR The value v of a new SUV is given by the linear model $v = -3{,}000n + 36{,}000$, where n is the number of years after it was purchased. Find the n-intercept and the v-intercept of the graph of the equation. What information does each intercept give about the SUV?

Use the intercept method to graph each equation.

35. $-4x + 2y = 8$

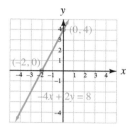

36. $5x - 4y = 13$

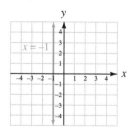

37. Graph: $y = 4$

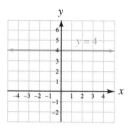

38. Graph: $x = -1$

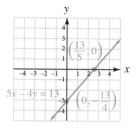

39. Solve the equation $x + 2y = 6$ for y, find three solutions, and graph it.

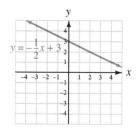

40. $7x + 3y = 0$

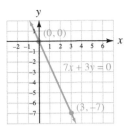

41. Consider the equation $3y - 2x = 12$. Explain in detail how each of the three methods that can be used to graph this linear equation. Which method do you prefer? Explain why.

42. RENEWABLE ENERGY The equation $p = 50s - 300$ estimates the power output in watts from a propeller blade turbine driven by a wind of speed s miles per hour. What information does the s-intercept of the graph of the equation give? (Source: otherpower.com)

43. LANDSCAPING A developer is going to purchase x trees and y shrubs to landscape a new office complex. The trees cost \$50 each and the shrubs cost \$25 each. His budget is \$5,000. This situation is modeled by the equation $50x + 25y = 5,000$. Use the intercept method to graph it.

  a. What information is given by the y-intercept?

  b. What information is given by the x-intercept?

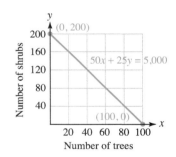

44. HOUSEKEEPING The linear equation $A = -0.02n + 16$ estimates the amount A of furniture polish (in ounces) that is left in the bottle after the sprayer trigger has been pulled a total of n times. Graph the equation and use the graph to estimate the amount of polish that is left after 650 sprays.

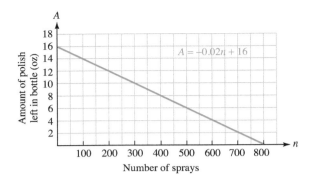

45. ENDANGERED SPECIES The number n of endangered plant and animal species in the U.S. during the years 2000–2010 is estimated by $n = 9t + 960$, where t is the number of years after 2000. Graph this equation and use the graph to predict the number of endangered species in the U.S. in 2022. (Source: *The World Almanac and Book of Facts, 2010*).

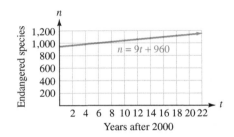

46. Find the slope of the line passing through $(-1, 3)$ and $(3, -1)$.

47. Find the slope of the line.

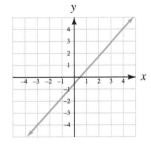

48.

49. What is the slope of a horizontal line?

50. RAMPS Find the grade of a ramp that rises 2 feet over a horizontal distance of 20 feet.

51. One line passes through $(9, 2)$ and $(6, 4)$. Another line passes through $(0, 7)$ and $(2, 10)$. Without graphing, determine whether the lines are parallel, perpendicular, or neither.

52. When graphed, are the lines $y = 2x + 6$ and $2x - y = 0$ parallel, perpendicular, or neither?

53. What is the slope of a vertical line?

54. Graph the line passing through $(-2, -4)$ having a slope $\frac{2}{3}$.

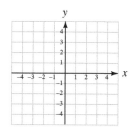

In Problems 55 and 56, refer to the illustration that shows the elevation changes for part of a 26-mile marathon course.

55. Find the rate of change of the decline on which the woman is running.

56. Find the rate of change of the incline on which the man is running.

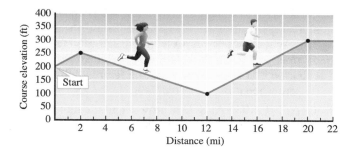

57. Another notation that is used to define slope involves the symbol Δ, which is the letter *delta* from the Greek alphabet. If the change in y is represented by Δy (read as "delta y") and the change in x is represented by Δx (read as "delta x"), then:

$$m = \frac{\Delta y}{\Delta x} \quad \text{where } \Delta x \neq 0$$

Refer to the slope triangle shown on the graph.

a. Find Δy.

b. Find Δx.

c. Find $\dfrac{\Delta y}{\Delta x}$.

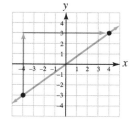

58. DEPRECIATION RATE A computer system was purchased for $25,000. Five years later, the value of the system had decreased to $9,500 . Find the rate of depreciation over that time span.

59. ROOFING Find the pitch of the roof.

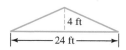

60. PHYSICS Suppose a particle begins at 0 on a number line (scaled in centimeters) and it steadily moves to the right in the positive direction. The particle's position on the number line for specific times is graphed below. For example, after 0.2 seconds moving to the right, the particle's position was at 40 cm on the number line. The **average velocity** of the particle as it travels along the number line is defined to be

$$\text{average velocity} = \frac{\text{change in position}}{\text{change in time}}$$

Find the particle's average velocity between 0.3 and 0.4 seconds.

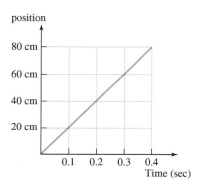

61. Find the slope and the y-intercept of each line.

a. $y = \dfrac{3}{4}x - 2$

b. $y = -4x$

62. Find the slope and the y-intercept of the line determined by $9x - 3y = 15$ and graph it.

$m = 3$, y-intercept: $(0, -5)$

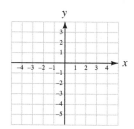

63. Write an equation for the line shown here.

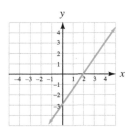

64. COPIERS A business buys a used copy machine that, when purchased, has already produced 75,000 copies.

   a. If the business plans to run 300 copies a week, write a linear equation that would find the number of copies c the machine has made in its lifetime after the business has used it for w weeks.

   b. Use your result to part (a) to predict the total number of copies that will have been made on the machine 1 year, or 52 weeks, after being purchased by the business.

65. DEPRECIATION After it is purchased, a $15,000 computer loses $1,500 in resale value every year. Write a linear equation that gives the resale value v of the computer x years after being purchased.

66. WATER BILLS For billing purposes, a city water department measures the amount of water used by a homeowner in hundred cubic feet (abbreviated HCF). One HCF equals 750 gallons. The company charges a base fee of $48 per month for up to 15 HCF. Then they charge $3.97 for every HCF used after the initial 15 HCF included in the base fee. Which linear model could be used by the company to determine the monthly cost c for a homeowner using g gallons of water when the customer uses more than the 15 HCF?

   i) $c = 48 + 3.97(g - 15)$

   ii) $c = 48 + 3.97 + (750g + 15)$

   iii) $c = 48 + 3.975\left(\dfrac{g}{750} - 15\right)$

   iv) $c = 48 + 3.97(750g - 15)$

   v) $c = 48 + 3.97\left(\dfrac{g - 15}{750}\right)$

Find an equation of the line with the given slope that passes through the given point. Write the equation in slope–intercept form and graph the equation.

67. $m = 3, (1, 5)$

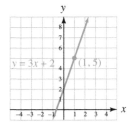

68. $m = -\dfrac{1}{2}, (-4, -1)$

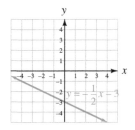

Find an equation of the line with the following characteristics. Write the equation in slope–intercept form.

69. Passing through $(3, 7)$ and $(-6, 1)$

70. Horizontal, passing through $(6, -8)$

71. CAR REGISTRATION When it was 2 years old, the annual registration fee for a Dodge Caravan was $380. When it was 4 years old, the registration fee dropped to $310. If the relationship is linear, write an equation that gives the registration fee f in dollars for the van when it is x years old.

72. TRAFFIC SIGNALS City growth and the number of traffic signals for a certain city are related by a linear equation. Records show that there were 50 traffic signals when the local population was 25,000 and that the rate of increase in the number of traffic signals was 1 for every 1,000 new residents.

   a. Using the variables p for population and T for traffic signals, write an equation (in slope–intercept form) that the transportation department can use to predict future traffic signal needs.

   b. How many traffic signals can be expected when the population reaches 35,000?

73. THE ATMOSPHERE The scatter diagram on the next page shows the amount of carbon dioxide in the Earth's atmosphere as measured at Hawaii's Mauna Loa Observatory from 1960 through 2010. A straight line can be used to model the data.

a. Use the two highlighted points in red to write the equation of the line with t being the number of years after 1960 and P is in parts per million of Carbon dioxide in the atmosphere. Write the answer in slope–intercept form.

b. Use your answer to part (a) to predict the amount of carbon dioxide in the atmosphere in 2020.

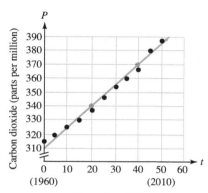

Years after 1960

Source: National Oceanic and Atmospheric Administration

74. DEPRECIATION A manufacturing company purchased a new diamond-tipped saw blade for $8,700 and will depreciate it on a straight-line basis over the next 5 years. At the end of its useful life, it will be sold for scrap for $100.

a. Write a depreciation equation for the saw blade using the variables x and y.

b. If the depreciation equation is graphed, explain the significance of the y-intercept.

75. Find the domain and the range of the relation: $\{(-4, 0), (5, 16), (2, -2), (-1, -2)\}$

76. Determine whether the relation defines y as a function of x. If it does not, find two ordered pairs where more than one value of y corresponds to a single value of x.

a.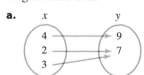

b.

x	y
-1	8
0	5
4	1
-1	9

c. $\{(14, 6), (-1, 14), (6, 0), (-3, 8)\}$

d.

x	y
1	9
2	9
3	9

77. Determine whether each graph is the graph of a function. If it is not, find two ordered pairs where more than one value of y corresponds to a single value of x.

a. 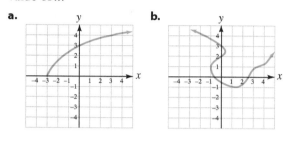 **b.**

78. For $f(x) = x^2 - 4x$, find each of the following function values.

a. $f(1)$ **b.** $f(-3)$ **c.** $f\left(\dfrac{1}{2}\right)$

79. For $g(x) = 1 - 6x$, find each of the following function values.

a. $g(1)$ **b.** $g(-6)$ **c.** $g(0.5)$

80. For the given input, what value will the function machine output?

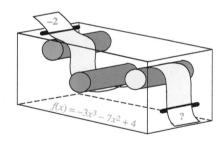

$f(x) = -3x^3 - 7x^2 + 4$

81. Complete the table of function values for $f(x) = 1 - |x|$. Then graph the function.

x	$f(x)$
0	
1	
3	
-1	
-3	

$f(x) = 1 - |x|$

82. ALUMINUM CANS
The function
$V(r) = 15.7r^2$ estimates
the volume in cubic
inches of a can 5 inches
tall with a radius of r
inches. Find the volume
of the can shown in the
illustration.

5 in.

8 in.

83. CONCESSIONAIRES A baseball club pays a
vendor $125 per game for selling bags of peanuts for
$4.75 each.

   a. Write a linear function that describes the
profit the vendor makes for the baseball club
during a game if she sells b bags of peanuts.

   b. Find the profit the baseball club will make if the
vendor sells 110 bags of peanuts during a game.

84. WOOD PRODUCTION The total world wood
production can be modeled by a linear function. In
1960, approximately 2,400 million cubic feet of wood
were produced. Since then, the amount of increase
has been approximately 25.5 million cubic feet per
year. (Source: Earth Policy Institute)

   a. Let t be the number of years after 1960 and W be
the number of million cubic feet of wood
produced. Write a linear function $W(t)$ to model
the production of wood.

   b. Use your answer to part (a) to estimate how many
million cubic feet of wood the world produced in
2010.